KU-346-375

SCREAM, IF YOU WANT TO GO FASTER

(NEW WRITING SCOTLAND 9)

SCREAM, IF YOU WANT TO GO FASTER

(NEW WRITING SCOTLAND 9)

Edited by
HAMISH WHYTE
and
JANICE GALLOWAY

Association for Scottish Literary Studies
with support from
Wm Teacher & Sons Ltd
Scotch Whisky Distillers

Association for Scottish Literary Studies
c/o The Department of English, University of Aberdeen
Aberdeen AB9 2UB

First published 1991

© Association for Scottish Literary Studies
and the contributors

400699

MORAY DISTRICT
LIBRARY SERVICE

F

ISBN 0–948877–12–X

The Association for Scottish Literary Studies acknowledges
with gratitude subsidy from the Scottish Arts Council
and the support of Wm Teacher & Sons Ltd
in the publication of this volume

Typeset by Roger Booth Associates, Newcastle upon Tyne

Printed by AUP Aberdeen

CONTENTS

INTRODUCTION

We're pleased to say that NWS 8, *The Day I Met the Queen Mother*, was a sound success. For a brief worrying moment there was the possibility that NWS 9 would not appear. Problems are always associated with lack of money, but it was the added reluctance of one or two members of ASLS to appreciate the value of such an anthology that gave us pause for thought. This may or may not be the place to voice internal grumbles, but it is certainly the place for us to affirm our commitment to new writing as a priority. 'Scot Lit' as a cosy study of the past is not enough: we must still support the vital and volatile brat that is literature in the making (whatever the trauchle involved). Academic research, as consolidation and testimony, might be necessary for a strong sense of national literary confidence, but it's worth nothing if it spawns nothing new, new work, new ideas: it's simply self-defeating – and that's one Scottish tradition we should put behind us. We are happy to report that ASLS reaffirmed its avowed aim of promoting the *writing*, as well as the study, of Scottish literature, and *NWS*, with continued funding from its sponsor, continues.

This year, then. In *Scream, If You Want To Go Faster*, we offer a broad selection of work: Edinburgh dirty realism alongside Gaelic thoughts on Chernobyl, Paris and Abyssinia, Eliot-cum-80s political pastiche beside an experimental M8, poetic celebrations of MacCaig and Leonard and a Sore Thumb, double-joints and reefers, sexual energy and sexual ambivalence, burning rubbish sites and watermarks, irony, tenderness, humour and crackling anger. And for those with a sweet tooth there are huge wobbling bits of chocolate, apricot slice (in the People's Palace) and Pandora's box of Maltesers. Regrets are, as before, the need to keep within our page ration, and that we still don't receive enough Gaelic submissions or writing by women. Let's hope we can do some catching up on these – and begin to look more assuredly forward – next year.

Janice Galloway
Hamish Whyte
June 1991

NEW WRITING SCOTLAND 10

Submissions are invited for the tenth annual volume of *New Writing Scotland,* to be published in 1992, from writers resident in Scotland or Scots by birth or upbringing. Poetry, drama, short fiction or other creative prose may be submitted but not full-length plays or novels, though self-contained extracts are acceptable. The work must be neither previously published nor accepted for publication and may be in any of the languages of Scotland.

Submissions should be typed on one side of the paper only and the sheets secured at the top-left corner. Each individual work should be clearly marked with the author's name and address.

Submissions should be accompanied by two stamped addressed envelopes (one for a receipt, the other for return of MSS) and sent by 31 January 1992, to:

Maggie Beveridge, Managing Editor *NWS*
c/o Dept of English Studies
University of Stirling
Stirling FK9 4AL

Kate Armstrong

FOR MY SON'S WIFE

Folding old cotton sheets to give you,
I hope you will know
the turn-on of a freshly made bed
as we do.

These are our twenties
and thirties, eased up from the foot
of the linen press, to be
measured, laid out

and buried. Some have shrunk.
The singles are less worn.
The doubles are patched in places.
My mother passed these on
to us. Cotton is nice to sleep in;
needs ironing. It lasts well.

Good luck. They are heavy
but fold surprisingly small.

NEGATIVE IMAGE

I don't really know why we settled here. I don't like commut-
ing – who does? – and sure, I know Londoners do, all the
time, far greater distances and so on and so on, and I'm only
talking about fifty miles. But there's no railway, of course, and
in the early days I knocked up more than enough miles anyway in the troughs of business life, phoning up people picked
from the yellow pages and touting for their business. They all
ought to want advertising, I thought. And I got the odd green
light and would drive hundreds of miles to convince a small
town businessman that he really needed a professional job –
mine. Mostly they couldn't afford it. I needed the bigger ones,
but we couldn't afford the prestige office rents in Aberdeen,
where the oilmen have bumped up the cost of everything from
real estate to raspberries, and anyway I had this notion we
ought to start small. You want to work for yourself – you pay
a price. Several prices. Living in the sticks is paying a price.
You can live without art galleries and casinos. You can't eat
foreign films.

So here I am. I spend a fortune on petrol, and on paying
Al's salary, and I live in this little seaside town, and get up
really early, earlier than most, anyway, to drive through this
fabulous countryside that I can't properly look at.

The fields are huge, and they *roll*. Your eye travels up from
the roadside, a very ordinary roadside with a barbed wire
fence and a ditch and a straggle of strawy greenery, and then
on and up. I once stood pretending to be bored in a fabric
shop, with Louisa, and watched the salesgirls hefting material.
Looking at these fields reminds me of that day. They're like
giant bolts of corduroy being slowly unrolled. And then
there'll be this great blue sheet of sky stretched behind it, and
one of those bare trees stuck just right up the skyline. Like a
mathematical diagram. A great wedge of brown field, and one
long dead straight stripe of fence and field-edge driving up it,
and the tree just off-centre.

It wasn't long before I started taking the camera with me,
and I'd just pull off the road by a gate and spend five minutes
there any day that the light was right. I can't describe what it
was like, taking photographs again just for the hell of it, after

all those ghastly days when Al was too drunk to let near a
client, never mind get the pictures for a brochure, and I'd
have to juggle things and people like crazy and rush off to do
it myself. Al's a better photographer than me when he's sober.
It was magical, standing in that clean, slightly salty air, and
not a soul around, and that faint smell of earth. The only person I ever saw there was an old boy on a tractor – slowed
down to pass me, had a good look and drove on. Putt – putt
– putt. The picture I got that day was like an abstract paint-
ing. Just those two slabs of colour, the heavy brown and the
silky blue, and the line, and that tree, almost purple.

There were other fields, and I took pictures of them too,
but that one had something. I did various large prints in Al's
darkroom. Ten by eight looked the best. My father loved it,
though he hasn't painted for years. So I did a print of it for
him – plain mount, non-reflective glass, no frame. And my
sister-in-law went a length about it, too, so I'd to do one for
her. She kept going on about how I should get up an exhibition, she knew various galleries would show them and sell
them and so on. She doesn't live in the real world. No con-
ception of what it's like running your own business. Anyway
she loved the field. She made a tapestry picture of it, for my
birthday. It was quite nice, though it didn't entirely work, for
all the print was so textural. I put it on the wall, for a while,
at home. Dave just glared at it, the first time he came round
for a drink, and said nothing.

I couldn't tell you what is Dave's sort of picture. Selling
garish watercolours to tourists probably blunts his sensibil-
ities. No, that's not fair. I was a bit disappointed when he
didn't immediately take to the photographs. Pleasant enough
about it, but he didn't think they would sell. I didn't push it, I
hardly could, but I felt worse, not better, when he downed his
third gin and said, 'Tell you what, give me a couple and I'll
see. Yes, you pick – any two.'

So there they were in this nice little shop – I'm tempted to
call it a 'shoppie', like the locals do. Their speech is marvel-
lously eccentric; go down by the harbour any day and listen
about a bit, and you could be in a foreign land. Even the ones
with a bit of education still speak – well, I couldn't tell you
what they call it. Their 'speak', I think. But Dave's not local,
of course. I thought he and I might have a bit in common. It's

a good site on the High Street, smallish, plain frontage, plain
varnished astragals, a few well chosen flowering plants in the
window, some nice round stones from the beach, and these
over-colourful little paintings of quayside houses, fishing
boats, puffin at sunset – that sort of thing. And lots of natural
wood finish inside, and more and bigger hideous pictures, and
those odd elbow-joints of sample frames strung up, and those
he does sell, all the year round. Does quite a lot of framing
jobs. Weddings and graduations and the like. My pictures
looked like nudists at a crinoline party in that company.

Even if we had hit it off better, I have precious little time
for socialising. Louisa got into the local life a bit, what with
the playgroup and tradesmen coming to do up the flat. Then
she started coming into the office a few days every week, to
man the phone – to woman the phone sounds quite indecent,
doesn't it? Thank God she's not a libby type. She was really
useful, when things got busier, and the little lad went to nursery. But one way and another, I forgot about the photos –
well, not forgot, but put the notion on the back shelf, and
determined not to think about it, or ask Dave.

So it was at least six months later, in September, when the
space invaders had gone back to wherever they come from
and left our place graveyard-quiet again, that I went for a
pint one night and met Dave. He mentioned, quite laid-back,
that one had sold. Yes, to one of the dreaded 'towrists'. It was
a good feeling. These awful childlike urges kept popping up
in me to ask, 'What sort of person was it?' 'Did he say anything about it?' 'Did he just hand over the money without a
word, then?' or even, 'Which one was it that sold?' He
wouldn't have remembered. But even so, I felt almost good.
You work yourself to a frazzle, trying to make a name, estab-
lish a reputation, look smart, learn when to joke and when to
be serious with clients – and then something you once did for
fun lollops back round a corner and stands there grinning and
wagging its tail at you. And that was that; I had sold a picture, we were busy; Louisa had a nasty bout of 'flu; I saw
nobody. Not socially.

Business did improve, after a lot of incredibly hard work.
I stopped having the performance with the yellow pages, and
the telephone rang a lot oftener. Al did some fantastically
good camera-work, but it was a brochure which I'd done the

photography for that brought us our first Norwegian job. I went over there for three days, by invitation. Nice country, terrific food, and they knew what they wanted and were prepared to pay for it. It was great coming home, though. I looked around that 'wee toun' with its boutiques that closed for the winter and its tractors in the main street, and these hordes of farmers large and small – mostly small, large small men – that come driving in from the sticks on Saturday, just like a proper market day, and I felt really pleased with myself for living there.

Like many people, I tend to put on weight when things are going well. Shortly after my return, I called Dave to arrange a game of squash. He said there had been a little old man in the shop, the previous Saturday. He'd been in a few times. Farmer. Aged about fifty-five or sixty. Flat 'bunnet' on his head, old raincoat, wellington boots pretty mucky, obviously not well off. And every time he came in, he'd sort of potter about the place restlessly, and end up looking at my photograph. The one with the brown field and the line of fence, Dave said. He only came on a Saturday, but he must have called in three or four times. And the last time the shop had been empty the whole time, but for Dave, and the old boy had said that that was his land, in the picture, and he liked the photograph, and was thinking about it. But he wanted to bring his wife in and show it to her. Well, farmers don't much buy artwork, so Dave was surprised when, the following Monday, the old couple appeared. The old chap in his grubby working clothes, and the wife in hers. And she looks at the photograph and she says to her husband, 'Ye doited old fool, what for d'ye want a photo of it when ye have the land itsel'?'

I took Al out for a drink that night. Perhaps a pub-crawl's more the word for it. That's one thing the place has plenty of. And I do remember that we seemed to meet someone we knew – or got to know – in every single one.

'Hello there again, Al! Long time no see, meet Joe Bloggs. It's Jack, isn't it?' Isn't it? Yes, it certainly is. Was. Plain blotto, stanco, over the eight to the power eight. No, I don't know why I put a brick through an old body's front window at eleven thirty-five. More effective than a hundred business cards. They all know me now. It was a stupid thing to do.

Elizabeth Burns

NOTES ON A PILGRIMAGE TO DUBLIN

A green-covered edition of *Ulysees* beside the bedside like a Bible, a portion read upon waking on Bloomsday.

Breakfast taken in a basement dining room, heavy with ornament, and having no windows. Going out from this into a morning splashed with sun and blue sky like a blessing.

Wearing white: white shoes, a shirt of softest cotton, made by an old Italian tailor, and the pale grey skirt printed faintly with irises and dotted with white. Sitting on a footstool in a bookshop with the wide skirt draped around, reading Irish poetry.

Eating, like Bloom, gorgonzola sandwiches in the pub at lunchtime. A Guinness-spattered copy of *Ulysees* lying open on a table. Joyce afficionados, drunk on port wine and words, spilling out into the sunshine.

The shade of a sycamore tree in Trinity College. Lying on the grass, skin dappled by sunlight falling through the leaves.

An actress in white lace, with a voice that is rough and magical, rendering Molly Bloom's soliloquy. The audience rising to their feet to cheer her as she utters the novel's final 'Yes'.

Taking coffee in the cool upper room, the museum, of Bewleys. A labeller of artefacts has added adjectives: 'a beautiful copper scoop', 'a magnificent silver cake stand'. Also butter churns, coffee grinders, tiniest teaspoons, a newspaper cutting from a day a Chinese clipper dropped anchor in Dublin harbour. The first chests of tea for Mr Bewley.

Taking a train out of Connolly Station to the country, to Rush and Lusk with its cream-painted waiting room with an old black-leaded fireplace. Murmuring of bees, paint peeling on benches too hot to touch, flowers growing round a green pillar box.

The Hill of Howth, watched from a hazed sea by the island of the Eye of Ireland. The slightest of breezes up there on the blue-facing cliffs, and wildflowers – campion, cornflowers, thrift, sea-thyme – and out of the scorched bracken on the cliffside new shoots coming up, bright green fronds still curled.

The GPO on Sunday morning, quiet and vaulted as a cathedral. The declaration of freedom as old as the desks with their inkwells, grooves carved out for fountain pens, and brass corners into which blotters once fitted.

Breakfasting in the stained-glass cool of Bewleys, then past the bright array of cakes and chocolates (purchasing on the way a packet of Irish afternoon tea: fine leaves that will make a strong and red-gold brew) and out into the stun of sunlight on Grafton Street, where a man is reciting Heaney and Kavanagh and people gather round to listen.

'There used to be swans, there used to be swans,' a little boy wailing as he leans across a bridge on St Stephens Green, sees only ducks.

Walking the strand to Sandymount, gathering pale finger-nails of shells, dabbling in rockpools warm as a bath. The shallow sea water so almost-hot that a steam is rising and floating above the sand, drifting inland.

Reaching Sandycove, his cove, his Martello tower, his round house with its clasp of cool walls and, up a spiral stair, its rooftop offering far views and a saltiness to the air. Inside, his inky-fingered manuscripts, his falcon-embroidered pink-gold waistcoat, and the round room where on September evenings a fire was lit.

Calm of summer evening in the wood-floored house of an artist. One of his five daughters suckling her big-eyed child, another offering salads and fresh bread. A third running bare-foot out into the garden, while their mother pours glasses of white wine and tells stories of her Dublin childhood.

An elf-like woman on Eccles Street, where once she was a schoolgirl. The school now disappeared, demolished by the nuns, along with that house, Bloom's house, the blue-doored number seven.

Making, on the dressing-table, a little shrine: the postcard from Sandycove (a drawing of 'Joyce recovering from his eye operation', hunched on the beach); shells from the strand; the green-bound *Ulysees*. The mirror behind, lace mats, a box of earrings.

Early in the morning, the fruit market on Moor Street, with its green gleam of apples, its snuggled peaches. A punnet of strawberries, eaten in the garden of the art gallery beside white roses, an abundance of them against grey stone, and a tangled plant of silver leaves.

Rust-red brick houses with doors of buttercup yellow under a blue sky.

Boys diving from Ormond Quay to swim in the river on a scorched morning when it seems the dark Liffey is the only cool place in the city.

Noontime, starchily hot. Bare-legged workers drifting off O'Connell Street to the Garden of Remembrance, to bask and picnic by the oblong pool, an oasis of turquoise water edged by low fences with gold harps and Celtic crosses wrought out of black metalwork: 'For those who gave their lives in the cause of Irish freedom'.

Walking the shady sides of the streets with Joyce's nephew, a gentle old man who wanders every day around old streets, pointing out houses once lived in, once written about, telling stories.

Out of this tenement on Mountjoy Square, he says, the writer's sisters looked with a telescope at the church clock, having no timepieces of their own. Frightened by their kinship with the infamous one, they ventured out seldomly, and when they did so, always crept close to walls.

Late afternoon, after dusty streets, washing with lemon soap that by now, like Leopold Bloom's, is a little melted from the sun. Feeling the body cool and lemony as a thread of breeze stirs the lacy curtains and lets saunter into the room the scent of windowbox flowers – pansies, fuchsias, sweet peas.

The moon above the Liffey, making its waters glint and shimmer under the spindly curve of Halfpenny Bridge.

Sadness gathering around the shoulders like a shawl on leaving, the dear city having eaten up the heart.

Ron Butlin

A DAY AT SCHOOL (1979)

(from a novel in progress)

Only a minute to go – and there he was, staring out at the playground, his fists clenched white; trying not to think of Ann McLeod. Trying not to get a hard-on. He'd be eighteen next week. Eighteen years old, for Christ's sake: he'd been carrying this stiffie around for nearly half his life and was still no nearer doing anything with it. The bell would be ringing at any second. he had to think about something else: Queens' chances for promotion? The Scottish Referendum?

Ann McLeod. Her long hair, her breasts.

His whole body was rigid now. All-over lust, every single part of him wanting it. Wanting anything. He closed his eyes and there was just his dying for it, nothing else – not even him anymore. He opened them then looked again out the cloakroom window to read the graffiti brightening up the old science building opposite, it might take his mind off things: IRA, FTP, Mental Craigies Ya Bass. Around him first-years were throwing bits of soap at each other or spraying water everywhere by sticking their fingers up the taps – one bit of soap, one drop of water and he'd batter the fuck out the lot of them. Ann went with older men – she'd been seen in the back of a bus, the driver and conductor having her at the same time. She'd taken the conductor in her mouth, so the story went. At the Langfields terminus.

The bell rang. Geography. He was hard as a rock. He was diseased. As he turned to pick up his books from the shelf behind the basins *it* touched the porcelain rim. He caught his breath and remained there with his fists clenched, his toes curled – concentrating on geography, the referendum, buses and public transport in general. Really diseased.

'You coming, Steve?' a voice behind him asked suddenly. His friend Billy.

'It's just the way I'm standing,' he replied automatically, then turned round. If he kept his books in front no-one would notice. Notice his disease, that was. If he kept his mind off

Ann McLeod everything would be all right. They left the cloakroom to cross the hall and went up the main stairs while Billy told him about being sick on a cider and stout mixture the night before.

'It's called *Black Velvet*. I had five pints in the station buffet then straight out and all over the tracks. I was still honking when a train came in – one of the porters had to pull me out the way. Five pints is a lot when you see it all at once.'

Ann was sitting in her usual seat across the aisle from him. The luck of the alphabet. She didn't look in his direction when he sat down – she never did. She was getting her books out of her bag: jotter, atlas, *Faraway Places,* graph-paper, her pencil case. There was a plastic mountain on Meikle's desk, its brightly coloured layers were nothing like a Scottish mountain – amazing that Haggis-heid didn't try changing it for a tartan one. Out of the corner of his eye he saw Ann putting her pencil into her mouth as she glanced over her notes. She began sucking on it thoughtfully.

His toes curled again.

'Want a photie?' she demanded, abruptly turning towards him.

'No, I was just–'

But she had already prodded her neighbour, a girl wearing a Bay City Rollers scarf:

'Says he disnae want a photie. No very gallant, eh Kirstie?'

'Whae disnae?' her friend asked.

He was going red – he could feel it. A real beamer.

'Oh, *him*!' Anne's friend exclaimed looking straight at him. 'Disnae ken when he's well-aff. He'd get on better wi a photie, that yin. A slow developer right enough!'

The two girls giggled. The slags. He turned away pretending to be interested in what Haggis-heid was saying: 'Whereas in the Deccan of Central India...'

Another four months till the summer holidays. Four months stuck in a classroom in the South West of Nowhere, Scotland, getting himself ready to sign on. Twenty more weeks of plastic mountains and then nothing. Some life. It was only March yet most of his classmates already knew what they were going to sign on as: Billy as a storeman, Ann and her friend as radiographers – whatever they were. Some of the Einsteins in the back rows were planning to go to college before the dole. With all his bagging the school he must have missed a lesson sometime in the last five years – the one where everyone learnt who they were, the one that separated the tractormen from the doctors, the accountants from the plumbers. Maybe he really was a slow developer? But one part of him had stopped developing for the time being – thank Christ.

Haggis-heid was talking about faults. Half the coloured bits of the mountain slipped when there was a *fault*. The earth's surface was continuously in movement: '*Continental Plates*' he wrote upon the board then chalked up a swirl of red and green arrows and numbers. Four more months of this. To his right, Billy was busy copying everything down; to his left Ann had already begun upon a series of coloured lines, using the crayons, to illustrate her continental plates more clearly. Nearly one hundred and fifty days to go – with Ann McLeod beside him at every geography lesson, and him getting harder by the minute. A gigantic stiffie four and a half months long. Unbearable.

Three-twenty: half an hour till they got out. As far back as he could remember he'd sat in one class or another while someone went on about something: Continental Plates, the digestion of the dogfish, figures rotating around the y-axis, how to calculate the time taken to fill an emptying bath –

'Perhaps McCunn will explain this phenomenon to us more clearly. It seems so familiar to him that he needs take no notice of what I'm saying.'

Haggis-heid was claiming him.

'Well, McCunn, the incidence of shift in the San Andreas fault – your observations?'

His what?

'Or were you too busy observing the young lady to your left, perhaps?' The teacher looked at Ann and smiled graciously, 'A most pardonable *fault*,' he joked then turning back to him added fiercely, 'But not in my class!'

He clenched his fists under the desk – Ann and the Bay City Rollers girl were staring at him, grinning. He blushed again: another beamer, the second in ten minutes. Sweat was trickling down the back of his shirt; he clenched his fists tighter.

'We're waiting, McCunn,' Meikle continued, replacing the

mountain on his desk.

And he was likely to be waiting a long time yet – never mind the answer, what was the question? Not that it mattered a toss except that Meikle was an arsehole and Ann McLeod was thinking *he* was too. A diseased arsehole. It was school that did it – thirteen years he'd been there nearly, and look at him. Look at Meikle, for fuck's sake – there should be a government health warning stamped on his forehead: 'School can damage you for life'. The RE teacher once told him that when St Paul was in jail his handcuffs had fallen off and the prison doors unlocked at his touch – simply from the strength of his feelings. Well, *his* feelings were strong enough, strong as any Holy Willie's any day of the week – he wanted out. OUT. Before he turned completely pervert, so stiff he couldn't walk but pogo-sticked everywhere. All he had to do was get to his feet and leave. No-one would stop him. Maybe he'd even give the class a short speech: 'Geography,' he'd say while pointing to the wall-charts of rivers, crops, rainfall, etc and the model mountain; 'Geography – ' he'd repeat, ' – or Life!' Then out the door. They'd all be gob-smacked; dead silence for several moments then there'd be excited chatter at his bravery; Ann would sit motionless gazing after him in admiration, almost in tears and wishing she'd realised earlier about his hidden strength, his spiritual power. She'd be worshipping him. Meikle would be a broken man; he'd sit holding his head in his hands regretting his life wasted as a geography teacher, its emptiness, its –

'On your feet, boy, when you're answering a question!'

'But I've not said anything yet,' he replied before he could stop himself.

At this, Meikle came striding down the aisle between the desks and stood next to him. '"Not said anything" – a comedian, eh?' he shouted. He was furious. The teacher's spittle showered his face, and close-to he could see the birthmark on his cheek like a wound that hadn't healed properly.

'Look at me, boy.'

He did so.

'You're here to work – not to play the fool. Not to daydream. You understand? *Work* – understand?'

'Yes, sir.'

'Now get your books open – and pay attention. Right?'

'Yes, sir.'

Yes, sir. No, sir. Fuck you, sir.

Meikle went back to his plastic mountain and began labouring through another demonstration of a fault. This time he gave a sudden 'Crash!' when the layers slipped – making the rest of the class laugh out loud. Hyenas, the lot of them. He opened his jotter, gripped his pencil and began colouring-in.

He worked steadily for several minutes – then came to an abrupt stop. What the hell was he thinking about? He'd forgotten all about the fault marks and drawn a completely green mountain. For Christ's sake. It wouldn't rub out and he was nearly tearing the paper trying. But no go – it was green from top to bottom, an ordinary mountain – not a geography one. What now – start again, or make it *really* ordinary instead, really Scottish? Tartan it up a bit with a ruined castle on top, some highlanders in kilts and a few tourists? A bit of blue for a loch, black for a slag heap and hairy cow – brown? That looked more like it. Some football supporters – more blue – with a bubble saying 'Scotland, Scotland'! Two guys leaning against the slagheap like they were having a pint, a wee turret for a yankee sub in the loch; some rain. Was that the lot? A bit more rain maybe. Where should he put himself – with the supporters? or the guys getting pissed? or maybe doing a highland fling on the turret?

Haggis-heid was still droning on and next year's dole queue was still taking notes; he put his pencil down. The dreariness, the heaviness of it all. Ann was dutifully copying out details of the San Andreas fault – could she really have had it off with two people, and at the same time?

Within seconds he was hard again: what would it be like kissing her then undoing the buttons on her blouse? Stroking her breasts, sliding his hands up her skirt? Jesus, he couldn't stop thinking about it. Grabbing her and screwing her stupid. He was going out of his mind. He was sick – and going to be rigid for life. Or rigor mortis was more likely, it was killing him.

Ann looked up and smiled. She'd be disgusted. He was turning into a pervert. He'd be going around in a dirty raincoat soon, whipping it out every time he saw a woman. Especially her. But maybe she'd not be shocked; maybe she'd

pull up her skirt for him and – and – He had to stop before he
went crazy, or got locked up.

Ann pushed back a lock of her hair and then leant
towards him, still smiling.

Had she seen he'd got a stiffie? She could hardly miss it –
just about lifting the desk off the floor. Maybe she'd tell
Kirsty? Give them both a good laugh: the class pervert.

'Hm…' she said in a low voice.

If she leant any closer it would be bursting through the fly.

'Hm…' she repeated, 'You'll no want Meikle to catch you
with that. But I like it,' she added with another smile.

Jesus Christ, she *liked* it. Was that really what she'd said –
in her sexy low voice? Was she going to reach over for a quick
feel? He was nearly exploding; one touch would have him
shooting out all over the desk. There'd be nothing left of him –
just a smear where he'd been sitting. But to feel her hands on
him, or her mouth. Or her tongue licking him. Stop. Stop. He
gripped the edge of the desk, stared down hard at the green
mountain he'd drawn and tried desperately to think about
Continental Plates, the Indian Sub-Continent –

'The castle most of all,' she continued, 'but d'you no want
a wee flag on it maybe?'

The castle, a wee flag. His grip on the desk relaxed a little;
his hard-on was already wilting.

The period dragged on. And on.

'For these are my mountains!' Haggis-heid announced suddenly in a loud voice, he was off again. 'The Floo'ers o
Scotland,' he glared at them. 'And now that your parents have
seen fit to throw away their chance of self government and the
only hope of political maturity in this country for the next
hundred years – ' he broke off to say 'The Floo'ers o Scotland'
once again, with scorn. 'We'll be nothing but a nation of Oor
Wullies, Peter Pans and Wee MacGreegors for a long time to
come. Not a grown man among us. Weans wi a Whitehall
faither!'

There was silence, Haggis-heid was a bammer – a real tartan bammer. His face had gone so red with anger that the
birthmark had almost disappeared, the danger signal was
when it vanished altogether. Someone was going to get a hard
time – but so long as it wasn't him.

All at once Meikle stopped in mid-sentence, paused as if

to get control of himself, then turned to the blackboard and wrote 'The San Andreas fault' in large letters. He broke the chalk twice.

'Now – ' he faced the class, a new piece of chalk snapped in his hand, 'Where exactly *is* the San Andreas fault?'

No response.

'Seeing as today is the worst day in Scottish history since 1707, I'll be easy on you. I'll give you a clue. The answer is Colorado – ' he paused for several seconds ' – or California.' Another pause. 'They're both in the States, as I'm sure you all know,' he added. The sarcastic bastard. 'Now take your pick: Colorado or California?'

There was still no response.

'Which is it?' he asked again. 'Hardly a difficult question. Even the dimmest among you has a fifty per cent chance of getting it right.' Meikle's gaze passed along the front row, 'Or wrong,' he added vehemently. '*Fifty per cent* – mair at least than the forty per cent they gied us.' His accent changed and there was menace in his voice. Like always.

No-one wanted to answer. What was he talking about – forty per cent?

He gazed around the room again. 'Paterson?'

No response.

'Hastings?'

No response.

'Third time lucky,' he announced as he looked along the length of each row to pick his real victim. Eventually he called out.

'Ah, yes – our fault expert. Steve McCunn.'

The bastard – it wasn't fair, he'd done his bit already.

'Have a guess then,' Meikle encouraged.

'Mmmmm – '

'Yes?'

Everyone in the class had deserted him – he could feel it. That terrible silence all around him. He was on his own: it was one to one, him and Haggis-heid. If he got it wrong Meikle would really go for him – and if he got it right the rest of them were ready to nod their heads like wally-dogs.

'Yes – ?' repeated Haggis-heid.

'Col – ' he began hesitantly waiting for the reaction.

'Col – ?' Meikle prompted with exaggerated politeness.

Now that he had calmed down his birthmark again stood out in clear relief.

'Cal – ' he tried this time.

'Come on, boy. Guess!' Haggis-heid was bating him to get it wrong.

Cal – or Col – ? He'd no idea. Cal – seemed to make him angrier, and so –

'Col – ' he stated at last, crossing his fingers. ' – Orado,' he added.

Not that it mattered. He knew instantly that he was wrong. Meikle's silence was like that of the mountain he'd been showing them earlier – before it burst apart, before the landslide, the avalanche, the earthquake, the erupting volcano.

Then it came!

'You stupid – stupid – stupid boy,' he roared out suddenly. 'Eedjit! Baaheid!' he screamed at him as he raged in a temper up and down in front of the blackboard.

What was this bammer shouting at him for? Who cared if it was Col or Cal? What the hell did it matter? Just because Haggis-heid was having a bad day *he* was expected to suffer for him. For this bammer – this head bammer in a roomful of bammers. Just because Scotland had had a bad day – but what the hell did that matter? Scotland was nothing anyway. A dead end. It was just history – not a real place like on TV. He wanted to grab Haggis-heid and tell him to take a running fuck to himself, him and Scotland the both of them. He wanted to stick one on him to shut him up. But he couldn't; he couldn't do fuck all at school except get stiffer and go out of his mind. To fuck with it – he was leaving. That day. At the end of that period.

When the bell rang he gathered his books together. A few of his classmates gave him sympathetic glances, indicating Meikle. To fuck with them as well. He stood up, left the room and dumped everything he was carrying – books, jotters, trigonometry case, the lot – on the first window-sill he came to and walked towards the main entrance. A moment later he was standing on the pavement in the afternoon sunlight. It felt great.

Marianne Carey

CITY NIGHTS, LIGHTS, SIGHTS

Saturday night a herd of yellow buses
Spews its contents into Hope Street.

A wash of grey city
Pours out across the pavement,
Smelling of musk and leather.
Two boys with heads like hammers
Lurch up the hill to the pictures.
One of them has Yankee Busters printed on the back
Of his jacket.
Moon-faced girls stalk the street on pointed feet.

At ten past eleven noisy queues clamour,
Greedy for pizza.
Upstairs on a bus in Union Street
A drunk man in a pork pie hat fishes through his chips for the
Pickled onion.
His red-veined eyes bulge
At his own reflection in the black window.

One o'clock in the morning.
Heaving dancers jerk through the noise
And clammy air,
Open their wet mouths
Then drift away to join the taxi queue
And lick the plaque
On other peoples' teeth.

A yellow Sunday ebbs to afternoon.
Down by the Clyde a man walks his dog
Past screwed up Wimpy wrappers
And a six-pointed star of grey sick.

MOVING OUT

Under the blankets
She scents the wet, animal smell of their closeness.
She hears him far off,
The fine spray and the soap's hollow thud as it falls,
Bouncing on the enamel.

(If I lie here I might never get up)

The water stops,
She pictures the rime of talcum,
The strong white hardness about him.

(I suppose he deserves better than this
I shouldn't expect him to understand)

He bends to kiss her eyelids.
– Are you getting up? You'll be late.
He is gone.

(Because unhappiness is more than just not being happy)

He crosses the room, whistling,
To leave a cup of pink tea beside her.

(If he came home one day and I was gone)

– I'll see you tonight.
His shadow above her shifts and is gone.

– The phone bill came, he calls.
I was right about buying stamps
It's nearly paid for itself.

The heavy door bangs behind him.

She throws back the covers,
Reaching for his dressing gown.

(Sometimes when I close my eyes
I can't remember his face)

Her feet make sticky, slapping sounds
On the bathroom floor.

Susan Chaney

SISTERS UNDER THE SKIN

She handed me back my past, this woman sitting next to me. She offered it to me casually as if it were a plate of sand-wiches, this woman I hardly knew.

'Do you remember?' she said. 'The smell of the dust in the old barn.'

Yes I remembered the chalky smell of the warm dust and the way the light filtered down through the derelict windows and the feel of the cobbles pressing through the thin soles of my sandals. I wrote my name on the wall, in shaky, sprawling letters. Like any young child who is learning to write I owned everything with my name. With passionate conviction I swept the floor and filled the manger with fresh hay and oats. I knew that if only I made the stable habitable again then a pony must come to occupy it. I was six years old. My logic was faultless and my will absolute.

Suddenly I felt uneasy. How much more did she know? Did she know everything? Did she know how eventually I gave up waiting for the pony and how my heart broke with disappointment? I could never go back to the stable again. I felt a superstitious fear of her, as if her knowledge were a cam-era and she could steal my soul away with it. She had already stolen so much. The silver horseshoe from my Christening. My first boyfriend and the second. She had always been two years older, always one jump ahead. 'You were horrible to me when we were little,' I said. 'You made me ride the farmer's pig. You dared me to take my pants down on the vicar's front lawn. You always betrayed me. Once in Assembly you farted so loudly that everyone turned to look and then you pointed at me. Worst of all you sent me down to Pascoe's for the milk when it was really your job to go.'

She laughed and settled down in her seat. She drove fast with one elbow resting on the open window, a style of driving that I usually associated with men.

'Oh, come on Jenny,' she said. 'Surely that's all par for the course isn't it? The oldest child is always pretty ruthless to the younger. It's called Sibling Rivalry. I expect I was jealous of you because I thought that Mum spoiled you. You didn't really mind that much, did you?'

'You can spare me all that Freudian crap,' I said. 'It doesn't impress me in the least. I did "O" level psychology as well you know. I hated you, it's as simple as that.'

Pascoe used to watch me as I tried to pick my way across his filthy farmyard. He would look maliciously amused by the sight of the green cow shit splattering over my bare legs. He was like a travesty of a surgeon in his green rubber milking apron and white wellington boots. He used to stare at my childish thighs where my sister's navy blue gym knickers hung down below the hem of my shorts. Inside the cow shed the air was thick with the steamy warmth from the cows and the sweet smell of cattle cake. He would beckon me closer to him and offer me the raw, wrinkled teat of the cow. 'Here ye are, Maid, it's your turn now. You can have a tug on her if you want. Mind you have to squeeze it good and hard.'

I could only shake my head, pull my hands away and hear my own foolishly polite voice saying, 'My Mother says will you please fill this jug for her?'

Then he would laugh and turn away, slapping the cow's broad rump with his large, purple hand. He would ease himself beside her, laying his face against her warm belly. Through the hot, red shame and the blood pounding in my ears I would hear the rhythmic drumming as the milk squirted into the metal bucket he held clasped between his knees.

I looked closely at my sister. Her profile was hard with concentration as she negotiated a difficult stretch of the road. She had my Father's nose alright, aggressive and determined but full face there was a winsome, vulnerable quality about her which puzzled me. It was most noticeable in photographs, as though the camera caught her unprepared, as though her persona of brash sexuality were a disguise that she wore for the world.

'How many men has she had?' I wondered. 'Dozens probably, maybe more. Perhaps as many as a hundred? A lot more than me anyway. If I were a man,' I thought, 'would I find her attractive? I don't think so. She's too taut and thin and her breasts look sharp and vulgar as if she's still wearing one of those 1950s style bras.'

I was physically very different from her, much heavier and

softer. She used to torment me and call me fat. She made me hate every extra inch of my body. Once she pointed to a woman with one of those giant pear shaped backsides often found on a certain type of Englishwoman.

'There you are, Jenny,' she said at the top of her voice. 'It's alright, at least there's one other person with a bum as big as yours.'

The night before I had been forced to undress in front of her as we had to share her sitting room floor. My children were asleep in her huge double bed with its decorative gold and white headboard. Rather an ostentatious bed I had thought for such a small flat. As I struggled out of my clothes I could feel Sonia looking at me. It was a look I remembered only too well from the past. She was leaning slightly forward, her dark eyes probing me from her semi-closed lids. A small smile played around her lips. She hadn't changed a bit, she was still as subtle and as wicked as a dentist's drill.

'You've put on a bit of weight since I saw you last,' she said.

I hadn't seen her for years, not since before my children were born. She had been abroad for a long time. I could feel that she was still watching me and then she saw the scar. My hands went instinctively across my stomach to hide the long ridge of red puckered flesh, the ugly scar that I thought I had come to terms with.

'My God! They made a mess of that didn't they? I hope you complained. I hope you kicked up one hell of a fuss. I would have. I'd have been bloody furious.'

'Listen,' I said. 'It's not the end of the world. It was an emergency Caesarian. As far as I'm concerned it's a small price to pay for a healthy baby. You've always been obsessed with appearances, that's part of your trouble. I don't have the time that you do to spend worrying about the way I look.' I stopped and indicated the bottles and pots full of lotions and creams that were stacked beside her bed. 'All your concern isn't doing you a great deal of good is it? You don't look so hot yourself.'

I thought Sonia was aging much faster than I was. Her skin looked drawn and grey and she seemed older than her thirty eight years. There was something sucking all the colour and vitality from her. She was collapsing from within. Another relationship was ending for her.

'All men are bastards,' she had said. 'I'll never trust another man.'

I'd heard this so many times before it was hard to know how she really felt about her break up with Philip.

I turned and looked at my children asleep in the back seat of the car. I knew that my face wore that shamelessly indulgent expression that all mothers adopt when their children are safely asleep and no longer bothering them. They were oblivious of what was happening, knowing only that Auntie Sonia was taking all of us to visit Granny by the sea. They slept on in a tangle of brown limbs and damp comics.

'She might have had a hundred lovers,' I thought. 'But I have got my children.'

The youngest one still clutched her bucket and spade. I leaned over and carefully disengaged it from her hand and as I breathed in the sweet fug of her breathing the ghost of my sister's aborted child materialised between us. It slapped me back in my seat with all the vicious energy of the poltergeist. Sonia would never have a child now. Her relationship with Philip had been her last chance. It was remorse and regret that were wrinkling her skin. Poor Sonia, perhaps it would be easier for her now that she had seen my ruined body.

The rain began as we crossed Bodmin Moor. I watched the windscreen wipers slapping backwards and forwards over the windscreen, flattening and releasing the beads of rain. We turned towards each other and said in unison. 'You can always tell when you're back in Cornwall because it starts to rain!' It was a moment of such unexpected intimacy that Sonia turned to me eagerly.

'Come on Jenny,' she said. 'I know we haven't always been close but let's try to be friends now shall we? Anyway it wasn't all bad when we were kids was it? We did have some good times didn't we?'

We had spent long Sunday afternoons crouched together in our favourite spot. Sitting on the warm concrete lid of the septic tank, which was splashed with crusty scabs of ochre coloured lichen, we were shielded from the house by the apple trees. Sonia would tell me long, involved and shockingly gory stories about unfortunate people who contracted rare diseases, usually in their rear ends. These would require a series of horrific operations culminating in amputation.

'But Sonia,' I would protest, 'that's awful! How could they live with their bums cut off? How could they go to the toilet?'

'Well the doctors make them new ones out of rubber, with straps so that they can fasten them on. Inside there are lots of pumps and tubes for getting the stuff out.'

'But doesn't it hurt a lot? And what happens at night? How do they get to sleep?'

'Well they take them off at night and leave them beside the bed like Daddy does with his false teeth.'

'I don't believe you... You're lying.'

Then she would muster all her authority and say, 'Listen, I'm two years older than you and I know about these things. I read about them in my encyclopedia.'

Sometimes we were friends and sometimes we simply needed each other because we were both children and the world was mysterious.

'Sonia,' I would ask her, 'do you know how long a minute is? Mum keeps saying: In a minute. In a minute. It seems to take forever.'

Then she would crouch down beside me, her eyes intent.

'Well I'm not sure, Jenny, but I think that when you are grown up a minute, or anything else for that matter, can mean whatever you want it to mean, whatever suits you best at the time.'

There had been one long, hot summer when hostilities between us were suspended for several weeks. It must have been something to do with the weather. We wandered the cliffs and the fields together where the flies danced above the dried, crusty cowpats and the dizzy, blinding scent from the gorse beat upwards on the hot air. Once we saw a fox on the beach. It hesitated when it saw us, one paw raised, its liver-coloured coat startling against the white granite boulders, and then it turned and raced back up the cliff and was quickly lost among the tawny reeds. We stood close together, wondering if we had dreamed but knowing that we hadn't.

As we drove into the West Country, I could feel my stomach tightening with tension. Now I could begin that familiar litany of names. Launceton, Parr, Portreath, Truro, Redruth, St Ives, St Earth and Penzance. I always had to come back, no matter what, I had to come back. I was addicted to the past and I was willing to drag my children six hundred miles from one end of the country to the other to satisfy my need for it.

Two days later and my sister pushed through a tangle of brambles and nettles and disappeared into the derelict boathouse we used to play in. 'It's all still here,' I heard her call. 'It's all exactly the same.'

I stood and let the past settle around me as I had known it must. I touched the dry, red soil and the sparse branches of the tamarisk trees which were flayed by the wind and the salt. I knew it all so well, it had become a part of me. It had always been a part of me. It was beautiful but desolate. A line of black rocks ran stark across the glare of the water. The stiff black bodies of the cormorants jabbed up into the skyline.

'John Thomas! John Thomas!' We had shouted as children and the birds would come hurtling down into the sea.

The place still smelt of rust and oil and damp rope. The lobster pots were smashed like ancient bones and the corroded bulk of the winding gear stood useless. From the fields came the familiar yet disturbing smell of decaying cabbage stalks. Winter and summer I could always feel that cold, purplish smell at the back of my throat. The red clay cliffs were dangerously eroded and the entire coastline was crumbling sullenly into the sea. A few more years and this place would be gone.

Sonia emerged, flushed and holding out a battered child's spade. 'It could have been one of ours,' she said. She bent and offered it to my youngest daughter but before she could take it I reached out and snatched it away.

'No,' I said. 'I don't want her to have it.'

'Why ever not?'

'Well, I don't really know, it just seems wrong to take it away from here. It feels unlucky to disturb things.'

'Oh, for Christ's sake, Jenny,' signed Sonia. 'Haven't you outgrown your morbid, superstitious imagination yet? Perhaps you thought it made you seem fey and interesting when you were younger but in a grown woman it's just plain bloody stupid.'

'I don't care, I can't help it, I just don't want you to give it to her.'

She shrugged, 'It's only a child's toy, not some cursed artefact from the tomb of Tut Ankhamen.' She waggled her fingers spookily in front of my face and made big, round eyes at me. 'It won't haunt you wherever you go and bring tragedy down upon you.' She dropped her hands, looking puzzled and a little sad and then she laughed.

'I know that you resent me, Jenny, but you needn't be afraid of me. I don't have supernatural powers. I'm not a fucking witch.' I turned away feeling confused and foolish. I didn't know what to do with the spade, it felt hot and heavy in my hand. It seemed too laboured and dramatic to replace it in the boathouse so in the end I flung it over the edge of the cliff, as far away as possible. I stood and watched it as it turned over and over in the air. It looked so gay and innocent with its scarlet paint flashings against the summer sky that I knew Sonia had scored yet another victory.

The past was rushing in unchecked. I had never lost my primitive fear of the power of inanimate objects. 'Things can't hurt me,' I had told myself all those years ago. 'Only Sonia and Pascoe and the rows between Mum and Dad can hurt me.'

We crossed the slipway and settled ourselves on the bench against the wall. It was ancient and the grain of the wood had been raised and coarsened by the weather. A few flakes of paint still clung to its surface and I still felt the same compulsive need to scrape them away with my nail that had been so strong in me when I was a child. I remembered hours of happy absorption with the warmth from the wood seeping up into my thighs and warming my insides, making me feel safe and somehow protected.

Sonia said, 'Do you remember the men from the village sitting here and watching us playing down on the beach?'

I remembered them, alright, those familiar faces from the past: Vernon Hicks, Charlie Trembath and Eddie Pascoe. Once I'd heard them discussing the drowned, naked woman they had hauled from the sea. They had been gutting mackerel and their hands dribbled blood and fragments of silver skin.

'Suicide!' they said. 'Wonder what made her do it?'

''Twas an awful waste,' said Pascoe. 'She was a fine looking woman. She had a lovely pair of big, hard tits on her. I wouldn't have minded giving her one myself.'

'And knowing you, Eddie,' laughed one of the others, 'you probably did an all, never mind that she were dead!'

Pascoe! How could I forget him? Once he trapped me behind the boathouse and parted my legs with his sly, hurtful fingers. I could still feel the shock of being dragged too suddenly from sunshine into shadow and the cold grasp of his hands on my sunburnt skin. Had Sonia known? She must have. She was everywhere. She knew everything.

I turned and looked out to sea. The tide was beginning to flow, the rocks were half submerged and a deep blue, fin-shaped ripple trembled out across the bay. I thought of the sea that beat inside me like a pulse. The same sea informed my sister and the same rhythm rocked in her blood. We had both been cradled in our mother's waters. Perhaps my mother had come to the sea, in the early morning when it lay calm and silky. Perhaps she had come when she was unable to sleep, when the restless child in her belly kept her awake. She might have come to this place to be soothed and comforted by the sea. My mother was of the sea and we were of my mother. I clenched my hands together tightly. 'My sister! My bloody sister!'

Two people were approaching through the soft, blue dazzle of the late afternoon. The woman's face had aged but I recognised her by the style of her dress; it was the full skirted, tight waisted style of the late fifties. Between the tops of her freckled breasts she still had the same crease of slightly greasy skin.

'Why, Bill,' she smiled. 'Isn't that the Lewis sisters? I do believe it is. I would have known them anywhere.'

It was one of those moments when time seems to stand still and everything happens in slow motion, when the space between thought and action is stretched to an unbearable tension. Once I had seen an old woman slip on the ice in a city street. I was too far away to call out or help in any way. As I stood and watched it had seemed to me that her falling was actually occurring in another time, another place. In the same way I now felt removed from my actions, as if I were only a spectator in this particular world and my acts could have no consequences.

I got up, slowly and deliberately. 'Look' I said, pointing to my children as they played down by the shore. 'Those are my children. Aren't they beautiful? Two little girls and a boy.' They admired them and then turned as I had known they must and looked at Sonia.

'How about you, Sonia,' said Bill. 'Do you have any children?' I watched with satisfaction as her face crumpled until all that was left was her look of wide open vulnerability and then inexplicably I found myself remembering the day that we had seen the fox on the beach. As I recalled the feel of her hand clutching mine and the way she had pressed her skinny body against me I began to feel that at last I might forgive her because after all she was my sister.

Barbara Clarke

CHICKENS

I don't expect you thought it would be me did you? I was such
a nice girl, so polite, always willing, wasn't that what they
said, always willing to lend a hand. I got the certificate for best
in helpfulness and conduct. I was the best but it didn't make
any difference, didn't get me one of those nice jobs, one of
those bank jobs where they have Christmas parties and go out
on Friday nights for drinks and go bowling together on
Saturdays. In the summer I heard they even went to France
and just for the day. Best in helpfulness and conduct, a worth-
less piece of paper.

It's easy for you isn't it? Easy for you to come here, it's
your job. I heard you had changed over to counselling, don't
suppose you had much choice. Must be strange being told to
go here or there, do whatever you're told, your duty to God. I
don't know how you stick it, how you don't just tell them all
to leave you alone. I don't suppose you remember me do you?
I was one of the good ones, who sang in the choir while
everyone else went home early. But I didn't have a home to go
to, not one that I wanted, not a place where tea was ready to
eat, not one of those places where sticky iced buns lay on
matching blue plates and boiled eggs were eaten out of matching egg cups. It wasn't like that in my home, but no-one knew
did they, no-one thought of reasons why I stayed behind for
drama and hockey even though I couldn't run very fast, or
read very well. Even though they all laughed at me. Remember
Samantha and Lucy , they went home to tea but they weren't
late, they didn't get a row or sent to bed without their tea.
They didn't have to wait for hours for buses in the rain
because mummy picked them up in the car. Well what do you
make of me, what do you think?

It was easy for me too, easy to cut with a knife, easy as the
sun on a porcelain butter dish, easy as squashing a butterfly
caught on a lavender branch. What will they do with me, what
can they do with me? I heard someone say it was working in
that place, full of blood and death. After a while you don't
notice. They put you on the firing range the first few days,

they're not allowed to, there's laws and unions but they put you there so you harden up quickly. If they don't people just crack and leave, or keep being sick. It doesn't get cleaned up properly, and then there's disease. At first the shrill cry from those chickens sticks to you. After they're stunned the feathers are ripped out. If you do it wrong they all fly up and hit you in the mouth. They look so strange moving down the line. They're already stunned outside in the packing shed, and then they come inside and move around on hooks, round and round and round, big bags of cold skin, their skin is pimply. They're scrawny things, but still their hearts are beating, you can see it throbbing inside the white soggy skin, just like frogs when they sit still on the edge of ponds. When you're new they put you down at the end where the chickens slowly come round on the hooks to have their necks wrung. They had to pad the pipes because people kept fainting. You stand there with the knife and slice through the gut, it's a flick, has to be at just the right angle so the guts spill out onto the plastic cloth, has to fall just right so the blood doesn't spill. In the beginning it's the smell. You work there fifteen minutes and you'll never get rid of the smell: You can go to parties or to the gardens, you can bath three times a day and smother yourself in perfume, the sort that doesn't rub off, but you'll never be rid of the smell. The ones who have been there years don't mind. The foreman, he's big and doesn't shave. He watches you, comes and stands behind you, close, so you can feel his breath, it's sticky like in the winter. He laughs, you can hear him laugh and you look up and he catches your eye and he looks hard, his eyes seem to marble over. He comes over again and stands still, he's watching you to see if you take your hands off the tray, or put the knife down, if you do you lose money, can't miss a flick of the wrist. He'll take the feet and claw your face, only as a joke. Later when I got used to the smell, it was seeing those eyes which had never seen a green field. Sometimes at home you find tiny feathers, stuck in your pockets.They're very soft, baby feathers which don't grow properly. I didn't think it would be like this, growing up, getting a nylon cap to cover up your hair and a discount on chicken breasts. It's an evil place. Never stops day or night, every day except Christmas day. Thousands of chickens hooked up going round and round with me closed into a place with no windows, paddling in death.

They think it happened a long time ago. Do you think I'll get off? I'd like some tea. Is it true what they say about nuns, do they really sleep in shrouds? I saw a nun once hold hands with a priest. It was Easter and we'd all stayed at school. We had a huge fire and all of us had candles. It was meant to be a laugh. We'd get a lovely meal on proper cloths and coffee from a blue jug and the Little Daughters, that was their name, they were all so fat and old with faces smooth and polished and yellow like the moon. They'd cut up the chocolate sponge and sprinkle more sugar on top of it. We were meant to pray for the new life. It looked lovely, reminded me of when I wore my long dress, white edged with lace from my grandmother's veil. But we all lit our candles and some of the nuns walked ahead, the cold night touching their necks, lifting their veils and the other girls dared me to run up and see if they really did shave their heads. It made me sad to think of them at night sitting on their beds unable to comb out their hair. It's such a special time, sitting on the edge of your bed combing out your hair. Do you know what it feels like to shake out your curls, let them dangle over bare shoulders right down to your breast?

My aunt told me that nuns used to bath in coarse sacks and weren't allowed to touch their skin, even to wash. But that Easter we were all praying, two hours in silence. It hurt somewhere. It was late, when we opened our eyes, I saw Sr Bridgit let go of Father's hand.

Do you ever touch? Are you ever lonely? Don't suppose you know. But you're not so young are you? What makes you believe in your god? Do you kneel down before a crucified man with a spear in his side, with those huge eyes, do you?

Do you follow a line of men who prostrate themselves three times to kiss a plaster cast, do you smear ash on your head, do you make up sins and give up sweets for lent?

What will they do to me?

No-one was there, no-one, not even God. Who's going to speak for me? Not God, not your small man tangled up in rope hanging from a rough piece of wood, rough justice.

It was easy. I know, you be the priest, you be the judge. I'll look you straight in the eye and tell you. It was easy waiting there that evening. I'd come in from work, I sat down at the table, didn't even put the radio on or the light. I like the early evening light, it's thin, reminds me of lonely times waiting for the front door to open and close, waiting for footsteps, waiting for kisses which don't ever come. It had been raining, the pavement was dulled and the outside lights made everywhere seem slippery. I still had my net cap on, still had my braising knife and I waited.

He'd be awhile and he'd come in wheezing, cigarette stuck in his mouth. He'd lay the paper on the table and fill up the kettle, then he'd balance the cigarette so he could take off his coat. He'd kick his shoes off and he'd say alright and where's the tea then?

When they found me they asked me why I'd never said anything about the bruises, about being locked in on a Saturday afternoon. They said I must like it, I heard them say it, they said she's kinky she likes it, an old fashioned man, they said he must love me and not to complain.

I showed them the chains and one of them laughed. He murmured tangle up in blue.

I stayed because one day I could put it right. I would somehow gather up all the badness and toss it away, like watching the ashes blowing away right over the cliffs far away. I spent a long time thinking about when it happened. I'd already put on my pink dress and gone to the dance and invited Sam back to my place and then later taken flowers to Liz. I'd send Sam a letter and he'd send me one and I'd keep it, it wouldn't get burned. In the summer I'd sit in the garden in the old bath tub remembering the time of going brown and making stories out of the faces in the trees.

When he came in that afternoon I was sitting waiting. He put his hand on my shoulder and bruised my neck with his beery breath. He could have been patting the dog. I lifted my hand up and flicked my wrist. I jumped back expecting his guts to spill out onto me but only a thin trickle of purple blood spilled out of his mouth. I thought of Christ with the spear in his side, but there was no water. He slumped down the way those big blown up clowns do. His eyes rolled up and then I did it again and again, hundreds of times, hundreds of flicks of the knife, each one for him stabbing me with his funny ways, each time stabbing and stabbing.

When they came in I was sitting in the pool of blood, it had started to dry. I heard the sound of some-one throwing up, I had started to pull out his hair. I was still wearing my overalls and my hat and I looked up and said is it break Sam, is it break?

That night I slept in cool sheets smelling of lavender and I dreamt of playing oranges and lemons at a birthday party. I was the last to get caught, round and round and round we went all laughing, all full of rich pink birthday cake. Right at the end I was caught ready to have my head chopped off.

Ken Cockburn: M8

Twenty-one orange telephones and three gaps

SOS
S1
SOS
S2
SOS
S3
SOS
S4
SOS
S5
SOS
S6
SOS
S7
SOS
S8
SOS
S9
SOS
S10
SOS
S11
SOS
S12
SOS
S13

sorrel

SOS
S15
SOS
S16

brown horse

UNNUMBERED
SOS
S19
SOS
S20
SOS
S21
UNNUMBERED

sheep, a gully beyond

SOS
S24

Pick Your Own Where People Matter Tricky Situations No waiting on verge No Loading Unloading at any time Request Stop Reduce Speed Now Warning Guard Dogs in Use Motorway No Pedestrians Vote Labour for Warrant Sales SOS S1 Hickson Contract and Retail Floorcovering New Road Layout Ahead Union Canal Clifton Hall School SOS S2 West Lothian District River Almond No Poll Tax in Independent Scotland SOS S3 Gulf What kind of fuel am I Frigo Scandia SOS S4 For Sale Ryden Fish Clovenfords 221 Police Patrol Vehicles Only SOS S5 Wimpey Plant Peebles Field Services ScotRail Uphall Good Food Good Ideas Iceland Abbey Chemicals Ltd SOS S6 Littlewoods ERDC 10 Millar Place Edinburgh Reduce Speed Now Muir Construction Fresh is Best Naturally Deer Park Quality Homes Visitors Welcome John Birnie Ltd Builders SOS S7 Yull and Dodds Ltd Impact Holidays Carlisle SOS S8 Deans Engineering Bruce Anchor Ltd RT Body Trades UK Another Design and Construction by Barr Construction Schlumberger Livingston Motec **TIMBER FRAMED HOUSE KITS** Radio Forth Radio Scotland Knowepark Caravans Bone Connel and Baxters Ltd Balfour Beatty SOS S9 Wm. Low Major Cold Store Distribution Depot Opening Autumn 1990 SOS S10 End The World's Leading Manufacturer of Cellular Telephones is coming to Scotland Fight for Ravenscraig Citroen Arnold Clark Safeway SOS S11 THL 498Y Tonto A Sound More Radio 1 FM Outstanding Service Amazing Choice Now we're motoring SOS S12 Safeway Tim Price Pontypool 04955 3038 Free Foresters Haulage Ltd Clift Burton SOS S13 Burnhouse Industrial Estate Murraygate Industrial Estate Radio Clyde Radio Scotland Metroglaze Barfab Reinforcements DCA ERDC Civil Engineering SOS S15 SOS S16 End LRC Price Metal Roofing Contractors Strathclyde Region FTP Football Coaches by Appointment Only Unleaded Supergreen Except Authorised Vehicles Thankyou for Calling at Roadchef Harthill Why Settle for Anything Less Quality Blinds Direct from the Factory R. Cairns Tarmacadam Contractors MGC Lowfield Ace Exhausts and Tyres Ross Good Family Food Lynx Take Care Whilst Leaving Vehicle Factory Let by Ryden Pioneer Transderv BOC Molly's Place Licenced Restaurant Bar Lunches SOS S19 Scottish Development Department A8/M8 Environmental Development Scheme Monklands District Motorway Maintenance Bensons Crisps P & O WH Malcolm Ltd Brookfield SOS S20 Central Scotland Countryside Trust Telephone Radio Clyde Radio Scotland SOS S21 Shotts School Boards Shottskirk Public Schools Uponor Central Scotland Woodland Project B192 WSR Lisa L Chooksey + Lisa IRA beautiful dralon bedroom furniture SOS S24 Thistle Removals Crown Sutherlands General George Fraser & Evans 0800 543 437 Jewson Terex Morton Machines Square Grip Key Catering Disposables Prestige Upholstery Smart Window Systems Thermastorm Britain's Best Double-Glazing Newhouse To Let Omega Training Ltd Honeywell The Scottish Lubricating Oil Co. Pedestrians Take Care Diverted Traffic Scotland's For Me! Pick Your Own Where People Matter Tricky Situations No waiting on verge No Loading Unloading at any time Request Stop Reduce Speed Now Warning Guard Dogs in Use Motorway No Pedestrians Vote Labour for Warrant Sales SOS S1 Hickson Contract and Retail Floorcovering New Road Layout Ahead Union Canal Clifton Hall School SOS S2 West Lothian District River Almond No Poll Tax in Independent Scotland SOS S3 Gulf What kind of fuel am I Frigo Scandia SOS S4 For Sale Ryden Fish Clovenfords 221 Police Patrol Vehicles Only SOS S5 Wimpey Plant Peebles Field Services ScotRail Uphall Good Food Good Ideas Iceland Abbey Chemicals Ltd SOS S6 Littlewoods ERDC 10 Millar Place Edinburgh Reduce Speed Now Muir Construction Fresh is Best Naturally Deer Park Quality Homes Visitors Welcome John Birnie Ltd Builders SOS S7 Yull and Dodds Ltd Impact Holidays Carlisle SOS S8 Deans Engineering Bruce Anchor Ltd RT Body Trades UK Another Design and Construction by Barr Construction Schlumberger Livingston Motec **TIMBER FRAMED HOUSE KITS** Radio Forth Radio Scotland Knowepark Caravans Bone Connel and Baxters Ltd Balfour Beatty SOS S9 Wm. Low Major Cold Store Distribution Depot Opening Autumn 1990 SOS S10 End The World's Leading Manufacturer of Cellular Telephones is coming to Scotland Fight for Ravenscraig Citroen Arnold Clark Safeway SOS 11 THL 498Y Tonto A Sound More Radio 1 FM Outstanding Service Amazing Choice Now we're motoring SOS S12 Safeway Tim Price Pontypool 04955 3038 Free Foresters Haulage Ltd Clift Burton SOS S13 Burnhouse Industrial Estate Murraygate Industrial Estate Radio Clyde Radio Scotland Metroglaze Barfab Reinforcements DCA ERDC Civil Engineering SOS

TiMber frAmed house kiTs
imber framed house kitsT
mber framed hoUSE kitsti
ber Framed hOuse kitstim
er framed houSe kitstimb
r fRamed hOuse kitstimbe

fraAmed HousE kits timber
raMed hoUse kIts timbeRf
amed house kits timBErfr
meD housE kits timbERfra
ed HOuse kits tiMbErfram
d house kiTs timbeRfrAme

house kits timBer frAmed
ouse kits timber Framedh
use kits timber FRamEdho
se kits timbeR frAmeDhou
e kIts timber frameDhous

kitS Timber framed hOuse
its tiMber framed hOusek
ts timber FRamEd housEki
s timbeR framEd houSekiT

timber frAmed hoUse kiTs
imbeR framed house kItSt
mber FRamed hOuse kitsti
ber fRamed hOuSe kitStim
er framed house kiTstimb
r framEd houSe kiTstimbe

framed house kiTs timber
ramed house kits timBerf
amed house kIts timbeRfr
med house kits timberFRA
ed house kiTs timberfram
d house kits timberfrAme

hOuse kits timbeR fraMed
ouse kits tiMber frAmedh
use kiTs tIMbEr framedho
se kits timber framedhoU
e kitS timber framedHOus

kits timber Framed hOuse
itS timber framed hOuSek
ts timbeR framed hOuseki
S tiMber frAmed housekit

TimbER framed house kits
IMbEr framed house kitst
mber framed house kitsti
beR framed house kitstim
er framed hOuSe kitstimb
r frAmeD house kitstimbe

frAmeD house kits timber
ramed house kits timberf
amed houSe kiTs timberfr
med house kits timberfra
ed houSe kits timberfram
D housE kitS timberframe

house kits timbeR fRamed
ouse kItS timber framedH
uSe kits timber framedHo
se kIts timber framedhOu
E kits timber frAmedhouS

kits timbeR framEd house
its timbeR framEd housek
ts timber Framed hOuseki
s timbER framed houSe kit

timber framed HOuse kits
imbEr frameD house kitst
Mber framed house kitsti
ber framed house kitstim
eR framed hoUSe kiTstimb
r frAmed house kiTstimbE

frAmed house Kits timbEr
rAmed house kits timbeRf
Amed house kits timberfr
med houSE kits timbeRfra
ed House kits timbERfraM
d houSe kiTs timberframe

house kits timber framed
ouse kiTs TimbER framedh
use kits timber framedho
SE kits timber framedhou
e kiTs Timber framedhouS

kits timbeR framed house
its timber framed housek
ts timber frAmeD houseki
s timbeR framed housekiT

matter

time

use   for   sos

road   ahead

fish

food   ideas

muir

fresh   best   deer   homes

trades

barr
radio

store

more

free foresters

estate

authorised

from

ross

take

bar

trust

shotts

ira

fraser

smart   thermastorm

for

matter

time   use

sos

road   ahead

fish

food   ideas

muir   fresh   best   deer

homes

trades   barr
radio

store

more

free foresters

estate

T. Cunningham

I'M SORRY, DADDY

Eleven years old, walking back from the farm.
Feeling proud, as a farmer's son.
Two hours there, a blessing to me after school.
It was fun, farmer's son, it was cool.

And it kept me away from that prison,
And two warders decidedly cruel.
With their hatred, I felt it was me, and their moans,
And their ham-fisted iron-clad rule.

She hated him then, that was all I knew. He was bad, he was
always drinking and being aggressive. She was okay. Why did
I think that? Because she was always moaning at him, goad-
ing, tempting, as long as she had someone, even a child to
protect her.

Anyway, I was coming back from the farm. It was a different world there. I could do virtually anything I wanted. I could
milk cows, kiss and cuddle some of them, clean out the byre,
wash the dog, pluck chickens, sterilise the milk and bottle it in
the farm's own bottles with:

John Owen
Cladden's Farm
Lenzie

printed on them in black. The bottles were quite unusual;
unlike the Co-op's, they had a slightly wider top, probably
because the rich could afford to put too much milk on their
muesli. Or was it the farmer's idea? Anyway, the gold tops
looked like real medals.

By the way, the farmer killed the chickens before I plucked
them. Sometimes, though, they would give a last parting kick
before they gave up their spirit and I would drop them on the
muck heap among the cow dung from the byre. I suppose,
looking back, it was ironic really, because my father hated
capitalists but could do absolutely nothing about them and
here was I, dropping their corn-fed, free-range, cock-bulled,
double-priced chickens among the cow shit. Dad would have

laughed at that one.

Lenzie was a very posh area, all bought houses. Dad would have said that the people were 'fat arses who had never worked in their lives'. He despised them.

They would arrive early on Sunday morning, in their fancy cars and pick their own chicken for lunch. They talked with the farmer in hushed whispers as if they could afford something illegal. The farmer would ask which chicken they wanted and she, to show her stupidity in culinary skills, would immediately point to the farm cockerel and say, 'We'll have that one with the head-dress and the stick-up tail, Eggbert, kindly inform the farmer.'

It's not the first time the cock had looked as if he was about to lose his balls when he saw outstretched arms pointing at him. You could see his eyes close and his head drooped a little. He stopped impressing the girls with his high kicks and military strut. Just for that moment, he wanted to be plain-clothed like them, and lame.

He should have known by this time that the capitalists always got one of the battery hens which were kept locked up in cramped cages in the dingy shed. There was always one that had stopped laying and couldn't earn its keep.

The subdued cockerel used to wander round to the muck-heap later and after checking that he'd escaped again, would practise his strut and deportment before rounding the shed to where the girls hung out.

Yes, I loved the farm and the farmer – he taught me a lot and so did the animals. My mother and father detested it. They could give me nothing so that's all I could have. They believed that they provided everything. The house was as cold as a whore's heart.

When I got home from the farm, my mother grabbed me in the living room, pulled me to the floor and whacked me on the head with one of my boots. My father was shouting, 'Hit him. Hit him,' so she whacked me another twice so hard that I felt that I must have done something terribly, terribly wrong. I just wanted to blurt out how much I liked working at the farm, I loved it. I didn't even know what I had done. I didn't have a chance to explain. I hadn't time to say I was sorry, to stall for a few seconds, to smile or cry, to protect myself. No. Whack – Whack – Whack. The heel of the boot drove mercilessly into my head. The lumps were huge.

They hated each other. I collected the consequences. I'd worn my new Chelsea boots to the farm – how disgusting – and I'd got them dirty.

No mercy for that wee bastard.

Fifteen years later, after being warned three times, Gillian, my daughter, drew a crayon picture on the living room wall. I jumped up. My marriage wasn't right. I despised my wife – she knew my weaknesses and played on them. I was in a misplaced rage at Gillian. I was frustrated, angry, aggressive and hateful. My emotions boiled over on to her. I would leather her, she squealed and her eyes filled up with tears as she looked at me – her slender body cowering with fear after seeing an anger she didn't know.

'I'm sorry, Daddy,' she screamed. My world turned upside down as I lifted her and held her close to my chest, my tears wetting her soft, shiny, innocent hair.

'I love you,' I whispered.

Children learn what they live. They can't always tell you about this vision of a perfect world that they have. They sometimes draw crayon pictures of it on your living room wall.

Talk to them about that picture, first.

MORNING

Early morning he gets up for his shift down the mine.
He hears her, shuffling round the kitchen.
The hangover pales to insignificance.
She'll start nagging immediately.
They religiously avoid eye contact.
It adds to the fun.

He drinks his tea as if it was the gift of life.
The patches on his moleskins peeled away,
Because the glue was fed up.
Skinny arms, yet strong, wiry like a miner's should be.
'You're putting your boots on the wrong feet,'
She snarls triumphantly, half laughing in her second of glory.
'I know,' he mutters, then says joyously,
'I should be fucking putting them on yours.'

John Dixon

PARTY TIME

Late nights and long leaves. It looks as if
spring's been pushing itself up again,
even the streets are struggling to get by.
They've no amount of trees for a start, big
green pillars that have been embargoed all
February, and people lapping light up
by the pint. It's a time for parties,
half-baked barbecues and compliments
on some obscure but compulsory wine.
The nine times out of ten tables
(and occasionally a chair) line their doors.
What will they say that hasn't been said before.

I can see what you mean, and it's easy to say,
but you're talking about this issue in a way
I don't like; as if people meant nothing; and why?
You're conditioned to think of society – thank
you Elaine, it's delicious my darling – as I
was once, so that what matters are things like the bank,
a new car, or the law; what Hildebrandt would call
an establishment view, although that's not all.

> Peter bought it yesterday
> at that Asian place Ann told
> me about. She likes it cold
> but you can have it this way
> too. It's true though, what you say.

Leonid liked his de luxe car, and took
it on a spin once a week. A police
escort would close all the roads, so's to ease
him into Moscow; and see no-one looked.

> People need more than an old-
> fashioned view of life to live
> now. Take me for instance – give
> me your glass Paul, it'll hold
> more than that – I've enrolled ...

Not that they'd lined all those woods so's to see
him (as the dead from some famine had done
underneath) only he needed this one
day off, as they did their lives, to be free.

If belief were enough I'd choose God, but it's not,
and can never be. Jesus Christ would have been shot
in South Africa; so please, don't give me all that
'There are more things in heaven and earth' shit, it's far
too divisive now anyway; take a look at
Northern Ireland – 'No honestly, I've got the car
to consider' – religion's just one great big lie;
I prefer: 'We must love one another or die'.

> Christ would have, made love I mean,
> that's what they forget at their
> garden fetes and 'Now a prayer
> for her Majesty the Queen'
> meetings. Isn't it obscene.

Krakow was taking the snow on alone,
it was as if the sky had gone on
strike, and ahead of itself in the one
go. So they buried the priest on their own.

> Whereas Christianity
> can be taken either way.
> As the communism they
> loath so much, or King of the
> Jews Show – come on Paul, for me.

Only the threat of a thaw that would show
them up for what he'd been, murdered and shot
at point-blank range made them change what they'd not
got on their minds, and dismember him, so.

They talk. They talk. They talk and talk and talk
as if the world could clean its kind of dirt
up at the dinner table. 'One more go –
I'll make it count tonight – before it's time
to put my hand up Mrs Burke there's skirt.
Now that, I'm looking forward to. She went
like an incinerator yesterday.
I might just shake her daughter up as well;
some fancy chat like this, a cigarette –
'you're looking so sophisticated' – and
who knows? I'll bet that bit of Auden'll
have helped me too. She's doing him at school.

If we don't we'll be so much emotionless ash
in another ten years. Now, their kids might be trash,
but mine aren't; and I don't think yours are. So, it's down
to us, either we love – and respect – what they are,
our tomorrows, or trade the one world that we've not blown
up yet in for a desert. I know which Ouija
I'd choose and … we must trust each other too. That's
what humanity means. It's not dying like rats.

    It's abominable Paul,
    I agree, but what can we
    do except learn from the
    Third World. Countries that can call
    themselves international.

Somehow the streets hadn't changed since he was
ten. It was true that the odd house had gone
and a museum been made of the one
shop, but then so what? He'd no sense of loss.

    Which reminds me: Melanie's
    off to India soon; this
    June, I think it is. She'll miss
    school, but then her sympathies
    lie more and more overseas.

Rather he thought it would always survive,
somewhere, at least; in an autograph he'd
faked, or the dark of his mind; but the speed
Pol's people burned it at burned him. Alive.

I've some books that might help her out there. She can come
up and see them. Just tell her to phone me, at home,
it's magnificent that; and she'll learn, as we all
did. I wish it were me! But to get back to what
we can do. There's a lot. Take that unethical
not to say – look Elaine, I'll be legless soon – not
to say tragic Angolan Aid programme; it may
have saved lives, but for what? The US useless A.

              Melanie's off to the States
              too, in Autumn. After that
              it's straight back to work. She sat
              her exams last week but hates
              all this tension while she waits

Now that the past had been stripped of his spare
light he could look at it from the inside,
only a stick of it hadn't quite died
so that the dark kept a kind of stake there

              for the results – so we'll
              see. I think she'll make it though.
              Which reminds me; I'll have no
              time to show you where the real
              ale shop is Paul. I don't feel …

Later that day he was led from his cell
and pantyhosed down to this post-
revolutionary style. It was the most
he would ever see of himself. In Hell.

Well, that's so sad. I think I'll go, no please
Elaine it doesn't matter. Ann'll be
expecting me. The children aren't that well,
and anyway – Whose car's that next to mine?
The bastard's parked right up my back
side – cunt – I'll disembowel him. Peter, you
know everyone round here. Get on the phone
right now, and tell whoever put it there
to ... right! That's great! OK. We don't know whose
antique it is; a crate like that, I might
as well just burn the bloody thing. I bet
he's scratched my paintwork too; he's close enough,
the prat. Just wait till I gold hold of him,
or better still the cops do; that'll make ...

Some day it will die this world, and the wind
dangle against it. The grass will go first
and then the earth. Deserts that thought they'd
re-order everything will draw to an end
and dark dawn on the evening. And that will be all, apart
from a storm or two; dust drifting where snows
did, and light left on
for a televised view of its own. Meanwhile the trees
strip to their tables, or pile up by the door.
If only they had leaves that we could take
out and make of another drawer.

Muriel Ferrier

Igp in the Iddlem

Cleaners brisk as bluebottles buzz round
the building, sucking dirt, exhaling words
that screech through funnels polished hard and proud,
that blast through plaster board boxes where yards
of wire snake after slip-on shoes. 'Hey youse,
d'ye ken...' I ken. I ken the tune, the news.

> Sandra's marriage
> > Fat belly carriage

> Thin grinning folk
> > At the minister's joke

> Virgin white dress
> > (Grey in the press)

> Keep them guessing
> > With God's blessing.

I know the secrets of their morse, fearsome
staccato clangs on heating pipes, jungle bells,
sophistical communication, known,
they think, to none but them, a way to spell
out warnings, pass the time, keep the Big Boss
wondering what they're at, bewildered with no gloss.

> Two quick two slow

> > May's gone to the loo
> > For a fag just a drag
> > (Skipping off what a bag)

> The boss won't know

> Two slow too slow.

My woman, Mrs Fraser, taps a can
of polish on the pipe. 'Workin late lass?'
'How's yer ma? She hasnae been this while back.'
'Fine,' I lie, drop an 'och' into the chat
like an owl pellet. Daughter of a char
I eat cod's roe and call it caviare.

Brown sauce on the sole
Score an own goal

Dinner at eight
From a second-hand plate

Reach for a pavement
Proper enslavement

Limp with the pack
No going back.

Pete Fortune

GREGOR COOPER DOING SOME TALKING

My friend Gregor Cooper called round to see me the other
night and straight away I could see there was something
wrong, knew it wasn't like him to be so agitated. Gregor runs
an off-licence in Academy Street and he told me he'd had a
customer drop dead on him that morning. He said it had put
the wind up him something terrible. I put the television off
and closed the curtains, suggested to Gregor we have a drink
and he could tell me about it. He declined, said a drink
seemed inappropriate, said all he wanted to do was talk. He'd
shut shop at lunch time and done little since then *but* talk,
but he reckoned he still had plenty of talking left in him. He
wanted to give his wife a break and he wondered if I'd mind.
I told Gregor Cooper to do all the talking he wanted.

He said this big bloke who couldn't have been fifty used
to come in nearly every morning and buy cans of Special
Brew and usually something else with them. Maybe a half
bottle of vodka or some cheap sherry or whatever. Gregor
said he knew nothing much about this man except that he
came in each morning and bought that amount of booze. He
had a notion the man's name was Albert, was pretty sure he'd
heard another customer refer to him as that one time. Albert.
He said Albert was certainly alcoholic but always polite, and
his manner of dress hinted at a lifestyle that had a degree of
stability about it. Gregor said Albert could never look him in
the eye when asking for his booze, averted his gaze in a manner which suggested something. Like he was probably
ashamed at that kind of intake. That morning when taking his
change though he'd looked Gregor straight in the eye, said he
didn't feel so well and was there anywhere he could sit down
for a while? He'd said that to Gregor and then kind of toppled
over a little, didn't so much collapse as lie down in a sort of
slow motion manner.

Gregor interrupted himself there and said maybe he
would have a drink after all, wondered how I was for whisky.
I poured us a couple of large ones and he got his story going
again while I was still in the kitchen. He said although this

big bloke, Albert, had always been pleasant enough, nobody in the shop had a good word for him. Gregor joined me in the kitchen, had folded his arms across his chest and was shaking his head. The licensed trade, he was saying, queer old business. It's our best customers we reserve our contempt for. I told him I could see how that added up, suggested we go back through and he could tell me some more.

So Gregor Cooper gave me this man who couldn't have been fifty, described how he hit the deck in slow motion and then lay there making little jerking movements. Gregor said he felt quite calm about the whole thing at this stage, presumed Albert was having a fit, the way a lot of booze fiends tend to. But when he got down on the floor beside him he became aware of blood trickling from his nose and then from his mouth, couldn't even be sure if he was breathing. He bawled at Lizzie in the back shop to phone an ambulance, said to tell them it was a siren job. Gregor was fumbling around trying to find a pulse, when all these horrible gurgling sounds came from Albert. He didn't know why exactly but he'd pulled Albert's false teeth out, got his tie off and ripped open his shirt. Gregor said he was into a sort of automatic pilot situation but then the gurgling sounds grew worse and all this blood and guts stuff came spilling out of Albert's mouth. Gregor said he'd never seen anything so horrible in all his life and I had no difficulty in believing him. He said Albert went all still and quiet after that and he knew he was dead, this big man lying there on his carpet on a Tuesday morning, and he'd just snuffed it.

I went into the kitchen to pour us some more whisky and Gregor followed me through. He told me he'd sort of straddled Albert, started pushing on his chest and then really thumping at it, but without having any real idea as to what he should be doing. He said he couldn't get it out of his head that he might hurt him. And all the time he was aware of the eyes, said they were wide open and it was like they were staring right into his. No matter how hard he tried not to, he kept meeting that vacant stare. Then he became horribly aware of being in close physical contact with a dead person and he just had to get out of it. Gregor said this was the first dead body he'd ever clapped his eyes on, but he didn't suppose it would be his last. He got himself back behind the counter and from there he could see Lizzie who'd just phoned the ambulance. He and Lizzie were the only staff in on Tuesdays. He said Tuesdays were a quiet day – nothing much ever happened on a Tuesday. Lizzie was coming through from the back shop and was looking at him, then at Albert on the floor, then back to him. Lizzie had both fists clenched and held in front of her mouth. She asked Gregor how the man was doing and he'd just glared at her, said how the hell was he supposed to know? Gregor said that right then he would have given a week's pay just to see some ambulance people come in his door.

He shook his head again, said he was drinking all my whisky and that he was sorry, wondered what I must make of him going on the way he was. I told him not to worry, said it was better to try and talk it out of his system and that's what friends were for anyway. I said all this in a loud voice because I was in the kitchen at the whisky bottle, but Gregor was right there beside me at the table again. I wondered what Gregor would do when I needed to go for a pee.

Anyway Gregor said Lizzie and him were just standing there and she was crying a little by now and saying surely there must be something they could do. He told her to go straight ahead, said he was sorry but he couldn't go anywhere near Albert. Then he heard the far-off wail of a siren, the new variety which always made him think of American TV films. He said he knew what it would make him think of in future, and it wasn't American TV films. So this ambulance came screeching to a halt outside the shop and Gregor said he recognised one of the ambulance people. This skinny little man who was one of Gregor's customers did all the talking, while his mate checked out Albert on the floor. Gregor said he was astounded in a queer sort of way when the ambulance man looked up and said there was no sign of anything, told him to stand out of the way. Gregor hadn't doubted it was a corpse he had on his floor, but the official verdict left him reeling. He wanted to know if that made any sense to me and I'd trouble convincing him it did.

So he got himself back behind the counter with Lizzie while the two ambulance men set to work with all their new technology, all this fancy stuff they had now courtesy of coffee mornings and fêtes and suchlike. Gregor said they tried to get

that heart going again, sent electric shocks and things into it,
but it was useless. He said they really tried but eventually
gave up, told him what he had better do now was phone the
police. Gregor told the ambulance men that Albert had been a
regular customer, revealed to them his alcoholism. The little
skinny ambulance man said it was quite a place for a wino to
breathe his last, and then he'd sort of chuckled. Gregor told
me he wanted to spread the little rat's nose all over his face
for saying that.

The little skinny ambulance man went through to the back
shop and phoned the police while his mate went out to his
vehicle. Gregor said a little crowd of people had gathered outside by then and they were jostling to see in the window, to
ogle the dead man on his floor. The ambulance man returned
with a sheet of some sort and covered Albert over with it.
Gregor said the two ambulance men kept referring to 'the
body' and that he couldn't accustom himself to that. He said
Albert had been up on his feet and alive not ten minutes ago,
said he was still the big bloke who came in each morning for
his Special Brew. And now he was 'the body'. He'd made
dying look easy; apart from the blood and guts episode the
whole exercise had looked effortless. Gregor said he'd been
mulling that lot over when the little skinny ambulance man
came back through, said the cops would be down shortly. He
suggested to Gregor that he lock the door meantime, reckoned
he could do without customers. Gregor wrote out a sign on a
sheet of card, stuck it on his door and then locked it. The sign
said *Closed due to Bereavement*.

Two cops appeared and rattled at the door. Gregor let
them in and it turned out one was a woman who knew Lizzie,
was married to her cousin or something of the sort. The male
cop asked Gregor a few questions, got some formalities out of
the way with the ambulance men, and then turned his attention to Albert lying on the floor. To the body. He went through
the pockets looking for identification of some sort, but there
was nothing to give even so much as a clue. Gregor told him
he thought the man's name was Albert but he couldn't be certain, and the cop just shrugged and said a lot of fucking good
that was. Gregor told me he thought that was no way to talk
with two women and a dead body on the premises. The cop
had another poke around Albert but soon gave up. Gregor

said the whole thing seemed really impersonal, and he got the impression that Albert being dead there on his floor didn't matter a shit. The big issue seemed to be nobody knowing who this booze fiend belonged to. Gregor had emptied his glass again, said imagine being such a selfish bastard that you drop dead without your name and address being tattooed across your forehead.

I told Gregor I was sorry but the whisky bottle was empty, said there was beer in the fridge if that appealed. He said it didn't matter, took me back to the scene in his shop. The male cop had done some talking on his walkie-talkie device while the ambulance men lifted Albert on to a stretcher and out to their vehicle. Gregor said the skinny ambulance man was so puny it was a miracle he could lift anything. Lizzie had started crying again and the female cop was trying to comfort her, suggesting they maybe take her home. Gregor said that was fine by him, said he intended to close for the rest of the day anyway. The male cop said they would be back in touch and then they were all off and out of it, leaving Gregor. He said he'd never felt so alone in all his life, said what was expected of you – being a man – was a right bastard sometimes.

So he decided to get out of there just as soon as he could. He was about to head out the door when he realised Albert's carrier bag was still on the counter, decided to get it and take it with him. He peeked in at the cans of Special Brew and the bottle of gut-rot sherry, added to them the assembly of small coins that would have been Albert's change. Then he remembered the false teeth and the tie, swept his gaze across the floor and located them lying beside some bin-end offer. Gregor said he could only look at the objects to start with, but eventually found the nerve to pick them up and drop them into the carrier bag. He looked in the bag again, saw some booze, a little money, a manky set of false teeth and a tie. He said it seemed to represent some sort of final statement, and that it didn't strike him as a very noble epitaph. Gregor leaned forward then and cupped his chin in his hands, kept shaking his head. Said maybe he would have a beer after all. He followed me through to the kitchen and kept going on about the carrier bag. All that was left of Albert was the contents of that carrier bag, he kept saying. That and a blood stain on the carpet.

I was curious about the carrier bag, asked Gregor why he'd taken it with him. He'd intended taking it to the police station, said it did belong to Albert after all. He'd paid for that booze so it should go with him, was part of his possessions along with the other stuff. The teeth and the tie. Gregor said that's what he had intended doing, but hadn't yet. Told me how he wandered about in a daze when he finally left the shop, couldn't stop seeing those eyes. He said Albert had made dying look so easy he half expected to drop dead himself any minute. Anybody could do it any time and he said he'd grown concerned about all the people he loved and cared for in the world. He offered me a queer grin then and said it was maybe best to ignore him, the mood he was in. I wanted to know where the bag was now, wouldn't have been surprised if he'd trailed it with him. He told me it was at home, said he must take it to the cops in the morning. Right now the bag was in the cupboard under his stairs, beside a briefcase containing all his important documents, insurance policies and things like that. He hoped his kids wouldn't go snooping around in it. He said he must have looked in that bag a hundred times by now.

Gregor came over all quiet and just sat shaking his head, cursing a little under his breath every so often. I was about to suggest we have something to eat but my wife arrived home from her evening class, looked in to say hello and asked Gregor how he was doing. He said he was fine, fed her some small talk about the kids, and then she disappeared upstairs to have a bath. Gregor half whispered to me that I could tell her his story later if I wanted, stood up and declared he had better head for home. He said he hoped he hadn't depressed me, told me to look in at the shop if I was up town tomorrow. I promised I would. He shouted a goodbye to my wife upstairs but there was no reply, and I explained that she wouldn't be able to hear him over all that running water.

I opened the front door for Gregor and outside it was freezing, the pavements sparkling white with frost. The bell chimes of an ice cream van could be heard drifting across from the scheme on the other side of the river. I told Gregor I would see him tomorrow and off he went, staggering a little with all that whisky flowing through him. I stood at my door until he reached the end of our street, then he turned the corner and he was gone. My wife appeared at the top of the stairs complaining about the draught, wanted to know if Gregor had called round for any special reason. I told her Gregor had been round doing some talking, that was all. Then I closed the door before any more heat escaped.

Raymond Friel

THE WIDOW

The drizzle.
The long-coated priest,
Draped in purple stole;
The closed book,

The hand raised
To sign a slow cross
Over the fresh grave;
The grave-diggers

Standing by,
Shifting in the cold,
Dying to get done
And get off home.

The widow
Was huddled away,
Her little dry sobs
Half comical.

Afterwards,
The doldrums lifting,
It was down the club
For refreshments.

A young lad
Balancing a tray
Of whiskies; a spread
By the Legion.

I sat down
With a sausage roll
And a beer, turning
To the old dear

Beside me.
I didn't know him,
No; it was my Dad's
Second cousin.

Aye, a shame.
In the wall-mirror
I saw the widow
By the buffet:

Glass in hand,
Having seen herself
In the same mirror,
White as a sheet.

I DIDN'T KNOW HIM

That remark
That day after tea
About the headlines
Sent me to the

Library,
Curious. I asked
For that year's papers
And sat, flicking

Through the months,
Long into the grey
Afternoon, until
I came to it.

The photo
Of the place; the wall,
Flecked with white, the slight-
Angled headstones:

The story
Of a local man,
Who died in the snow
In the graveyard;

How foul play
Had now been ruled out.
Making it what? Fair?
Somehow all right

That a drunk,
Taking a shortcut
Home, had cracked his head
And died frozen?

I suppose
It did, unless you
Knew the man, unless
He meant something.

They told me
The story then, re-
Luctantly. I might
Have been upset,

Or angry
For what he once had
And ruined; but I
Didn't know him.

Graham Fulton

PANDORA'S BOX OF MALTESERS

Outside
 the ALL-NIGHT Cinema
with stuffing sweating from razored seats
people are driving home to their beds.

 Inside
the ALL-NIGHT Cinema
full of dark and finger-fucking and farts
we settle down to watch PLAGUE OF THE ZOMBIES.

The horror around us breathes in.
We open a box of Maltesers.
The tear-your-ticket-in-half girl
yawns,
shines
a light into
            our eyes,
wanders back up
                the carpet aisle.

Dream-sequence zombies stumble about
with egg white eyes and dressed in sacks.
The cold sucks in our toes,
pastes itself
onto
our
skin
(but we'll be home in an hour

or six.)

Inside
the ALL-NIGHT Cinema
fat with whispered threats and cider shouts
the homeless children curl up for the night
inside their jumpers
and shirts.

Glasgow around us breathes out.
We settle down to watch LUST FOR A VAMPIRE,
open
a box of
Smarties.

PARIS

Forest of candles, stained glass saints,
fleamarkets stretching beyond the horizon

of sight, belief,
and mythical Frenchmen with tanned Sasha smiles
hassling every woman who walks
buzzing every piece of meat.

Stinking cheesy heat,
flies
     droning
              around
raspberry tarts,
butchers bins,
skewered dead be-headed chickens,
skins, peels, gristle and pips
and buckets brimming with filthy lather
slopped onto the pavement
and the men outside the sexshows
pulling the grinning, eager tourists
clutching their souvenir busts of Napoleon
into the parlours of strange positions,
temples of hot impossible things
and buskers singing
GUAN
        TANA
               MERA

as the sun slams down on smooth legs of girls
in loose summer frocks, swinging their hips.

Transvestites wearing the make-up
that barely conceals their pain,
and pointing into their open mouths, bobbing their heads
up and down and squeezing and patting
the groins of tourists
who don't know they've just had their pockets picked,
clutching their souvenir ballpoint pens
clutching their souvenir gargoyles
in the freak back-streets at sundown.

And the young brown couples splashing their feet
in fish-filled fountain pools,
and children playing on swings and chutes
and children letting ducks eat cake
and children sucking the final glow
from thrownaway butts of tourists
still clutching their souvenir teatowels,
clutching their souvenir Eiffel Towers.

Robespierre! Antoinette! Zola! Sartre! Aznavour!
A smell of onionsweat and dust,
fatmen in vests dragging on Gauloise
poor girl in black gargling like Piaf,
poodles straining at tether ends
madgirl in pink dancing on tiptoe,
forest of clients, white-boa whores
and buskers singing
GUAN
          TANA
                    MERA

in cool metro caves
as the sun smashes down on Gendarmes
wearing traffic-fume blue, swinging truncheons.

And negroes who look right through you
winding-up their clockwork birds
with ticking timebomb wings.
The old man swindled by life
on a bench beneath a breeze-rustled tree
in one of the boulevards of passion,
romance, sex, enchantment, delight.

The Lovers River nudging its flotsam
of used condoms against its banks,
and buskers singing
GUAN
          TANA
                    MERA

as the sun slaps the face of the girl on the train
breast-feeding her baby,
and shouting for money above the rumble
which nobody gives her.

OVERTAKING ON THE BEND

A piece of cucumber
floats in my tea

but it all goes.

I love these days
but not the wet
or dry ones

pigs look out
between the slats
in the back of
a slaughter truck
we pass; perhaps
they think they're
on holiday

returning through dawn
to the North
clouds
in spilt Fanta, concealed wine,
paper bags fresh full of puke,
undereye bags
and underarm sweat
of a fat-arsed steward
in turquoise slacks
who's had a hard day
but haven't we
all,
and someone is lurching
against the walls
inside the tiny
chemical bog

at the back
of the bus
they canni sing

trying to keep their balance
while whistling a merry tune,
trying to flush a shite away
and I should know because
it's mine.

My talents
do not stretch
to the mastery of
machinery,
logic, legend, bucket and spade,
sand in butter, parted lips,
custard, chips and
tricky clues,
the crossword waiting
to be completed
in record time
(It'll have
a long wait)

human looks out
behind the glass
in the back of
a luxury coach
we pass; perhaps
we think we're
on holiday.

I love these towns
but not the pretty
or grim ones

a piece of North
floats in my tea

but it all goes,
down the same way.

A SORE THUMB MARCHES
DOWN RENFIELD STREET

spins
every third or fourth step on
his heel,
a fuzzy brownsuit on his body
a baggy brownbeard on his chin,

a pile of paper under
his arm,
a blank expression on
his face
        with
the hint
        of a twinkle in those eyes.

And he keeps up
his gently demented progress
down
through
        workies' wooden tunnels,
        canyons of shoeshops
        winebars banks,
        tottering plank and
        scaffolding sculpture
        leading on
                to Central Station
        out of
            this moment

        forever.
        A planet

going the wrong
way round, a swimmer
against the pull of the crowd,
tailor's dummies and taxi cabs,
pigeons scattering to the sky and
dirty Glasgow sills
and ledges,
                making

some people smile, a little,
at two o'clock
in the afternoon rain.

Robin Fulton

SETTING OUT

The gravestones still weigh the same.
No-one has altered the dates.

No-one asks why I've come back
again. To see not graves but

that wedge in the river-bank
where the green boat leaned. My years

at home had boulders on them.
The keel never touched water.

My years away tugged at weight
no longer there. The ribs now

gave their atoms slowly back.
The boat is no longer boat.

Its ghost sets out at high tide.
Its wake is a coiling script

whose fluency the words trapped
on granite could well envy.

THE WATERMARK

The white light of the afternoon waves
throngs in.
The voices crowd in too, leaving no
corner
of air unagitated in this
creaking
wooden room whose windows ancestors
measured
to fit their view of unmeasured ocean.

Oblongs of piled rocks on the shore mark
common
graves. The ornaments survived the skulls.
From these
stones a light shines fainter than our eyes
can hold.
It is hard and survives ornaments.
It glows
through me to the unread watermark
I bear
from window to window and never see.

FOR SOMETHING LIKE A SECOND

It's weeks now, I thought,
since they've noticed me.
The dead, I meant. That night, then –
I'm fifty but back
where once I was five.
From the manse window I watch
a flat-topped beech-hedge
(which was never there)
and beyond it the black pools
(which were) flooded up
from The Black Water.
Father, gone four years, is back
too, but not thirty,
more like seventy,
ruffled, tired in mid-morning.
We're out of time with
time and place, our years
slide, bits of broken mirror.
But for something time
would call a second
we're in time with each other.
Beyond the crisp hedge
the unmoved black pools
turn white, answering the sky.

HIGHLAND PEBBLE

In the hand, found wanting.

There are more ways to growth
than obeying green cells.

In dreams I throw the stone
and it walks back. In life
I throw it and it stops.

In neither can I lift
what gives the stone its weight:
Ben Griam's westward scoop,
the wind's prevailing touch

and the tenacity
of water molecules
working through the peat maze.

A context, outliving.
A subtext, blind, writ large.

My hand, that's found wanting.

Jane Harris

HUGE WOBBLING BITS OF CHOCOLATE

First thing I realise this morning is I need fresh air so I crawl off the sofa-bed without disturbing Philip yeah. Though it'd serve him right, the bugger. The larger the man the louder the snore that's my experience. Looks like mine hosts are still asleep too, so I sneak outside. Delightful house. Super people. Shame I got stomach-ache and couldn't eat dinner. Mind you, dear Philip compensated for my lack of appetite. Not half.

Okay I find one of those shops that sell everything from detergent to Puff Candy and I buy some Auntie Flo's Tablet Cups. Seem to have developed a sweet tooth in my dotage. Have a walk a suck and a think. I detest this town. Yes, it's got a castle and some galleries but where's its soul, that's what I always say to people. I said that to Lynn last night. Don't think she was best pleased. The atmosphere was a little sour at times yeah. Maybe because we're working in the same theatre. On top of each other. Yes.

Anyway once I'm pos they're all awake I head for la maison. Philip is sitting in the living room with his back to the window, reading *The Times Literary*. Oh apt apt. I tap on the glass and would you believe, he closes the paper, folds it, places it on the floor, stands up, turns round and nods at me. Very decisively. As if he wasn't certain who might be scraping at the window. Who else does he suppose it'd be you know, and why didn't he just look over his shoulder? God.

Dear Philip. He's so methodical it drives me absolutely barmy. Once, he was stuffing taco shells with salad yeah, one little ribbon of lettuce at a time. But the lettuce didn't fit quite the way he wanted, so he'd tease it out and prod it in again. I just stood beside him at the worktop. Watching. For, ooh about 15 minutes. Of course there are other times, maybe when he's been particularly witty or clever, that I look at him and think: one could do a lot worse. Indeed, one has done. More often than one cares to remember dear.

After a bit more nodding he realises I want to come in. Not bad for a MENSA member ay? He opens the door, then scuttles back into the living room and hides behind the paper.

Lynn's in the kitchen making coffee, thank heaven. Her husband Dave is holding one of those multi-cereals, the ones where you get eight small packs you know each with a different kind of cereal in yeah. He looks absolutely astonished. Staring at the little boxes and shaking his head. 'I don't know if I can face these,' he says. He has a Dublin accent so everything he says sounds terribly caustic and thrilling.

'Have an egg then,' says Lynn.

'An egg,' says Dave. 'Would you like an egg, Robert?' he says to me with a glint in his eye, like a man suggesting we embark on a wonderful adventure together.

'No thanks. Just coffee,' I say. A quick coffee, big hugs all round, then leave. Pronto. Disappear. Philip can go to his bloody exhibition or whatever and I can shoot off home. You know what it's like, people stay overnight and in the morning they want fed again and they're under your feet and you think: God's teeth, when are they going to leave yeah?

'What about Philip? Would he like an egg?' asks Dave.

'I shouldn't think so,' I say. I smile. We're all standing very close together because their kitchen is quite small. 'You could ask him.' I only add this because I'm damn sure Phil will want to trot off to a gallery.

I follow Dave to the living room and can't help noticing how well made the dear boy is. I walk in, to hear him repeating after Philip: 'Some cereal, orange juice, a soft-boiled egg, not too soft, some toast and a pot of tea? That right?'

'That's right. That will be lovely,' says Philip. Dave slides past me, muttering Philip's order.

Well. I sit on the couch and stare into my cup. We shall be here for days. This is really de trop. Philip hoists his paper and folds it mercilessly. One would think we were strangers in a hotel lobby. He is being particularly irritating lately. If I didn't know it would look bad, I'd walk out now. Alone.

Lynn arrives with the cereals. She shows them to Philip.

'Which cereal would you like Philip?' she says. She's so polite. If I were her I'd cuff him across the face with the box.

'Ooh,' says Philip, grabbing it from her. 'Let me see.'

'Just pour the lot into one bowl,' I say. This is me taking a swipe at Philip's weight problem yeah. 'Crack an egg in. Marvellous for his coat.'

Philip laughs good and hard at that one. Hig hig hig. His

cheeks are pink and delighted. They meet his shoulders with no apparent pause for jaw or neck.

'Cornflakes would be lovely,' he says, handing Lynn the cereal box like it's a menu. I have to keep reminding myself not to clench my teeth.

Lynn fetches a metal tray. On it is a jug, a glass of orange juice and a bowl.

'Here you are Phil. Sit up,' Lynn says. She should have stuck to bloody nursing and left arts admin untainted.

Philip discards the *Times Lit*, rearranges his buttocks in the seat, evacuates his throat, swallows, then allows her to place the tray on his knees. No wonder I forget he's only in his thirties; there are times when he acts older than me.

'Okay,' says Lynn sunnily to nobody in particular, and goes back to the kitchen. I select a book and try to read but I'm somehow compelled to keep an eye on dear Phil. Call it morbid fascination.

First he takes the jug and pours a good helping of milk into the bowl. Not too much so that it's swimming. Just enough to cover the flakes. Next, he slides the spoon in there, getting the amount he wants, exactly. Drains off some milk. So it won't drip on the shirt front dear. Keeping his head very still, he raises the spoon and pokes cereal into his mouth. Then, he chews. One is instantly reminded of the sound of jackboots, marching on autumn leaves. I don't suppose he can help the noise really. After all, they are cornflakes.

As he eats, he gazes straight ahead through his specs; he could be watching his own reflection in a mirror. There's a dreamy look in his eyes. I often imagine him like this before we met, sedating himself with rice pudding and god knows what in that dreadful bedsit. He swallows, then shunts his spoon into the cereal and repeats the process. Until his bowl is empty.

One slug, and the juice is gone. He raises four podgy fingers to his mouth, puffs a couple of belches at them, and waits for someone to clear away his dishes.

Right on cue.

'Everything OK?' Lynn asks.

'Smashing thanks,' he says. 'Yeah.' He nods his head about seven times and purses his lips seriously, like he's thinking really hard about how smashing the cornflakes were.

'Good,' says Lynn. She takes the tray. 'More coffee Robert?' she asks.

'Yes please,' I say. 'I'll come and get it myself.' I glance at Philip to see if he noticed this last remark, but he's attempting, with a great deal of rustling and gasping, to tame *The Observer.*

Dave and Lynn are having breakfast in the kitchen. They're listening to the Archers. I pour coffee and tell them how super the book I'm reading is. I assure them we'll be off in two shakes. No problem they say. So sweet. I stroll back to the couch in the lounge. There seems to be nowhere else to go.

As I drink my coffee, I find I'm remembering when I was a student. Funny how the mind wanders. A group of us were in my friend Caroline's house. We were smoking. Talking. Caroline and her boyfriend Iain weren't getting on, they were pretty much at the end of the relationship by then. We were all eating sweets and this tiny piece of chocolate lodged in the corner of Caroline's mouth. She hadn't noticed yeah but Iain did. He was an American. I'll never forget him glaring at her with his lip curled, saying:

'Jesus Caroline. You've got huge wobbling bits of chocolate all over your face.'

But there was just this one little crumb. God. Not long after that they split up.

Hurrah! here's dear Lynn with a boiled egg, some margarine, a plate, a knife, everything he'll ever need for a cup of tea, and a teaspoon.

'There you go Philip,' she says. She sounds as if she's about to burst out laughing any second. But doesn't. Philip casts his paper aside, clucks till his arse is comfy, then accepts the tray.

'I'll bring your toast through in a moment,' says Lynn, 'Okay?'

'Yes,' says Philip. He sniffs, sets his breakfast on the floor and grasps *The Observer.* He's frowning. Dear dear. One can tell he's disappointed that the toast wasn't there, ready. On the tray at the same time as his egg.

'Here we are,' says Lynn coming back, 'Sorry for the delay; our toaster's broken.'

'Thanks,' says Philip, but he's reached an interesting article so he doesn't look up. Lynn tips the toast onto his sideplate.

'More coffee Robert?' she says.

'No thank you.' Actually I could murder a cup. I say this because I'm embarrassed.

'Okay,' says Lynn as she leaves.

I stare at my book. There is laughter from the radio in the kitchen. A panel game. I picture the studio audience in tidy rows, adoring the celebs, laughing on demand. Then riding home to Chigwell on the tube and telling the neighbours how funny it was. I watch Philip. He reads. And reads. He's not touching this breakfast yeah. After about a minute I put on my sarcastic voice. I say:

'I don't think Lynn is coming to butter your toast for you.'

He glares across at me. One can tell he's upset because he gets this twitch above his right eyebrow.

Still in my sarcastic voice I say: 'You might just have to butter it yourself dear.' Then I stick my head back in my book sharpish because he looks like he might burst into tears. That's all we need. Good Lord.

After a moment, I hear him grunt, hoisting the tray onto his lap; then there's a tapping noise as he probes the egg. When I look up, Philip isn't crying, he's inserting a hectare of toast into his mouth. His lips protrude, like he's wearing an African tribal accessory. He breathes loudly through his nose; one hand cups his chin in case anything drops onto his front. Only him and this breakfast exist.

When the food is all gone, he jiggles crumbs from his shirt onto the tray and returns it to the floor. He attacks the crossword.

Dave pops his head round. 'Cheerio now,' he says. Poor lamb works on Sunday. 'Lynn's getting dressed. See you both again soon.'

'I'll look forward to that,' says Philip, with a queenly wave from his chair. There's a great smear of egg yolk across his chin.

'Bye,' I say. As the front door clicks, I feel an acorn of pain in my gut.

Philip frowns into the paper. Soon, he'll spend some considerable time on the loo. The larger the man the longer the toilet-time yeah, so I've found. I go out and start the dishes. Might as well. While the basin fills with water, I worry about this pain. I'm just hoping it's not an ulcer.

Jane Harris

BEFORE THE WRESTLING STARTS

You can taste the blood and sawdust in your mouth. Women
line up along the chequered floor, shuffling from one tile to
the next. Behind the counter, men in white coats package and
serve meat.

'A pound of beef links please,' says the blonde in the
queue. The old dear. Cheesed off that I decided to come with
her for a change, after months shopping on her tod. I stand
behind her, my nose level with her armpit. Her coat stinks, a
mixture of cigarettes and damp wool. Sometimes I'm
ashamed of her, ashamed that she smokes in the street, that
she can't drive. Most of the mothers at school drive. Volvos,
at least. Even Tubby's old doll picks him up in a Merc. My
mum is carless. 'Better throw in the same of mince as well
Charlie,' she says.

Charlie is the one. He hasn't spotted me yet. Through the
glass-fronted counter I watch him manipulate bundles of flesh
on a sheet of paper. The mince is the same colour as his hands;
the sausages glisten with grease. Charlie flips and twists the
paper into a parcel then slaps it on the counter. His fingers are
plump, but fast.

'Mince and links, Mrs Cowan,' he says, showing his teeth.
Those teeth. Mangled and poking straight out. His nose turns
up at the end like it's disgusted at the sight of them. In third
year drama we played that game where you say what kind of
animal someone would be if they weren't human. 'Anything
else, madam?' says Charlie. Charlie would be a wild boar, only
more polite.

'What do you recommend, Chick?' says madam, flaring
her nostrils at him and making a low growling sound. The
old dear would surely belong to the big cat family. A panther
perhaps. She does this nostril flaring business a lot. Only at
men of course. Except dad, and only when he's off on sales
trips, earning my school fees. 'I pay the Academy fees, you
can damn well slog for your pocket money, sunshine,' so says
the old boy. Tough tittie, eh? But I suppose if it wasn't for the
paper round I'd never have met Charlie.

'How about a nice chop for your man's tea?' says the wild boar to the panther. This is what is chalked on the board in the shop window. 'HOW ABOUT A NICE CHOP FOR YOUR MANS SATURDAY T?' it says, and 'PLEASED TO MEET YOU, MEAT TO PLEASE YOU'. In the mornings, Charlie doesn't talk much. I only found out about him working here because I hid my bike and the newspaper sack after we finished yesterday and followed him.

'No, no chops, that's our lot thanks Chick,' says mum. She frowns into her purse. Maybe she's noticed there's a pound missing.

'Wait the now,' says Charlie, 'A wee mouthful for the lad,' and he shoves a slab of raisin dumpling into a bag, whirls it round to seal it and dangles it above the counter. So he did spot me. He draws back his lips, points at me with his teeth. Usually he doesn't smile much. Just a quick grin when he comes in. 'Hello Roddy,' he'll say, sort of shy. Then he closes the shed door.

The shed's in the garden of one of the big houses up the Crescent. We've been going there for about a month. Before that, I used to cycle past him. I suppose he was on his way to work and we nodded at each other: for some reason you feel you have to be pleasant to solitary strangers at the crack of dawn. I used to try and imagine where he lived, if he was married, that sort of thing. Then one day he was waiting for me on the corner with his fly open. 'Good morning ducks,' he said. Ducks. That was a funny thing to say and I knew he wanted me to follow him. So we went to the shed for the first time.

The old dear is spreading her nostrils again. 'Aw the nice,' she says. She thinks Charlie's giving me free grub because he fancies her. 'Go on, Roddy,' she pokes me. 'Take it.'

'Aye Roddy,' says Charlie, 'take it.' This morning, he hardly spoke at all except right at the end. Then he blasphemed a bit, and grunted.

As I reach for the dumpling, I realise he isn't going to let go. If I touch the bag we'll stand there, staring each other out, stuck together by a lump of suet and raisins until they come and yank us apart like a pair of dogs. There's a gleam in Charlie's eye, a sort of challenge, and for a second I almost believe I've blurted everything out. But it's my imagination.

The women in the queue begin to shift uneasily and someone clears their throat. It's my mother.

'Roddy, take the dumpling from the nice man,' she says, 'PDQ,' but just then Charlie relaxes his hand and the bag thuds onto the counter. Mum grabs it and slaps it in on top of the mince and sausages in her shopper. 'Och, Chick you never stop do you?'

'So they say, Mrs C,' says Charlie. He winks at the other ladies in the queue as mum leaves, then he looks down at me, his tongue flicking at a tusk in the front of his mouth and I know he's already looking forward to Monday morning. I squeeze past the queue at the entrance, trying to tell from the reflection in the glass door if my nostrils are flared. But there's too much condensation. Outside, the old dear is lighting up a Dunhill in the estate agent's doorway.

'Get your arse into gear, Roddy,' she says, pushing ropes of smoke out of her nose. She hates Saturday shopping. She always wants to get it over with ASAP so she can get our lunch onto trays before the wrestling starts.

A.L. Kennedy

WARMING MY HANDS AND TELLING LIES

'But it's such a wonderful idea.'

'Do you think so?'

'Yes. I mean, ten years ago – to have written that. The millionaire's house invaded by all the animals his jungle road had killed.Wonderful.'

'They weren't real animals.'

'Well, of course not, but you made that clear. The thing is, you made them have the effect that real animals would, I mean, we felt for them.'

'Felt sorry for them.'

'Of course. We were sorry. Those eyes always watching him; the constant sound of their feet. When that tiny armadillo drowns...'

'It drowns in the millionaire's toilet.'

'I know.'

'And you actually think that works.'

'Yes, I've said, haven't I? I think it's a wonderful story.'

'Mm hm. They're still making roads through the jungle, they're still killing animals, destroying indigenous tribes.'

'Well, one story...'

'Exactly. One story wouldn't change that. You're right.'

She was peering at him again, he didn't like that. She peered the way she would in front of a fish tank, checking to see if something might have died. He wondered what she was checking for in him.

'I know you didn't mean to say it, but you're right. There isn't any point in writing, because it does no good. It does nothing at all.'

'But that...'

'Means that I've wasted my life. That's right. Is that what you came to find out?'

'No.'

'Then why did you come?'

Well now, he was sure he'd told her why. He couldn't have been so nervous he hadn't said. He told her before he arrived, before he even came to Dublin. He wouldn't have come all this way without telling her first: a brief, careful letter, her glorious reply and then the phone call. Hearing that voice, almost unable to answer when she spoke that name, her name. She knew why he was here. She was being confusing, making him argue, making him say things he hadn't meant. It wasn't how he remembered her at all.

But, to be honest, how did he remember her? Monagh Cairns. Novelist and critic, Monagh Cairns.

She had come to his school, one Friday and read some stories. He could only recall a part of one.

Each night, the men and women of the city would go to sleep. Before they climbed into their beds, parents would kiss their children and weep and then they would walk, round shouldered, to lie under thin, cold blankets and wait. Sometimes wives and husbands would hold hands.

Each night, in one or two of the low, dark houses something very terrible would occur. Folk would point at darkened windows in the morning, they would stare at bolted doors. They would say, 'The Industrialists came there.'

He had written it down, maybe twenty times, each time slightly different, but mostly the same. And although he had searched through every source he knew, he had never found a story by Monagh Cairns with a passage like it. He had never found a story about night-time disfigurements, or invisible creatures called Industrialists. Perhaps he imagined it.

He hadn't imagined her. Lovely. He never could have imagined anyone so lovely.

Thanks to his later researches, he knew that she must have been forty or thirty nine. Her second and final husband had left her that Spring and she still had no children. She never would. Next Spring, her third collection would be published. Good reviews. For another six years, she would stay in Scotland, then she would go to Ireland and fade out of sight.

He was seventeen that year and when she arrived on the Friday, he was already waiting and watching and listening hard. He was there to make up for the others. Front row desk. He would show them he was good at something. They wouldn't understand her the way he did. He read books.

She surely must have noticed him when she stood so close to his desk. And maybe she felt something. He wanted her to feel how ready he was to understand exactly what she meant, prepared to be special for her, because she was special, too. Mr Haartman had already said, she was a writer. She did that and nothing else.

By the end of the afternoon, she had read them three stories, one of them very short and all about love. They were still in the silence after that story, having heard a woman talking, with their accent, about fears and excitements that didn't seem even likely in someone so old. She really knew about love. One of the girls made noises as if she might cry.

Miss Cairns; Monagh – you were allowed to call her Monagh – had asked them all a question.

'Are any of you interested in writing?'

He didn't put up his hand. Nobody did, but he wanted to, he wanted to very much. He had always prayed for a moment that would alter the whole of his life and now it had come. That question. Her question had made it come. Something hot seemed to fill him and he knew this was it, for sure. He imagined the change must be howling out of his ears and down his nose. His hair must be starting to lift and he didn't dare open his mouth, for fear of his change bursting out.

Monagh kept on speaking and he tried to catch her eye so that she would see him and know, by the way he was sitting, that really he wanted to write. As he remembered it now, she did look his way.

'Why did you come, David? I can call you David?'

She didn't seem very different, even today. Her hair was still a blonde that could be grey, or vice versa. It was long but wound about itself and sat very neat on her head. Once he had seen her wear a French plait in a television interview and there were photographs of her with a page boy cut and a perm. Sitting now in her living room it was odd to have only one possible image of her. She seemed, somehow, less convincing like this.

Of course, time had passed and that did make for changes.

After the move to Dublin, there had been no more photographs and five years had left her face surprisingly old.
Monagh's mouth seemed smaller and the line of her chin had
blurred. She peered.

'I came to see you, Monagh. I came... I thought I'd
explained. The article.'

'No, I don't understand, no one would want an article
about me. Not now. Scarcely then. You'd better, I don't know,
it's all very confusing for me. I'm not used to this any more.
How long are you here?'

'Two weeks.'

'Could you come back tomorrow, no, the day after. Come
back then; on Saturday. I've been ill, you see, otherwise I
wouldn't be at home. I have to work. Would you mind coming
back?'

'No, that's fine, I don't want to put you out, Miss...
Monagh. If I came after lunch.'

He'd met her first on the Tuesday, half past four, by one of
the ponds in St Stephen's Green. He was to wait in front of the
sign that explained the ducks. There were many varieties of
duck.

The plane brought him in from Glasgow just before
lunch. It didn't take an hour, not even an hour from his home
to hers. He could have done it any time. If he'd had the
money. Now he could afford the plane fare, just about, and a
fortnight in a reasonable hotel.

David's room was small, mainly pink and grey. It smelled
of disinfectant and chemically freshened air with a touch of
cigarette smoke underneath. He filled the kettle provided and
lay back on the bed, trying to let himself know he had arrived.
Turbulence on the flight had left him quite unsettled, but he
felt better now. What he should do, he should have a little tea
without milk, put on the radio for music and read a few pages
from 'Nobody There' – his favourite Cairns collection. That
would put him in the mood, on her wavelength, let him get the
feel of her. So to speak.

*They dusted leaves from each other's backs as they walked to
the car. She pulled little twigs and fragments from the sleeves*

of his cardigan and swiftly brushed her fingers over his hair.
Before they parted to open respective doors, she paused and
allowed him a chance to kiss her. He continued to walk and
fumble through his keys.

He dozed for almost an hour, dreaming of parkland and
hares with grey blonde fur. Monagh's forehead caught by the
classroom sunlight; somewhere he saw that.

It was raining quite sharply by the time he set out for the
Green. He had decided to travel without an umbrella, but
wearing a hat, because he felt more confident that way.
Umbrellas made him uneasy, they seemed to demand the use
of both his hands and he found himself clumsy in the street.
The hat and the long dark overcoat were much better.

He did want to look his best. For Monagh.

Striding out into the street, he knew he was at home with
the city; dressed to fit a Joyce short story, or a fragment of
Beckett prose; significant, stylish and a little out of time.

The way he had chosen took him through Merrion Square
and he wanted to stop there and look at a few of the plaques.
There was one to mark the house where Yeats had lived, one
for Wilde and another for Le Fanu. At school and constantly
reading, he had always assumed these people were
Englishmen. As with Barrie and Buchan or Sir Arthur Conan
Doyle, success had automatically made them English.

He noticed the plaque for Daniel O'Connell – not a writer
– but by this time he was running for the gallery steps. Over
the road and through the high gate and up the path to shelter.
His hat was beginning to droop and the bottoms of his
trousers were starting to cling. He mopped his face with a
handkerchief and blew his nose, his forehead stinging with the
cold.

He squeaked across the varnished floors, pausing in front
of a high, glowering canvas which took its theme from the
Book of Revelation. If David stared at it and partly closed his
eyes, the overall effect was strangely warming. He remembered Monagh Cairns took 'Revelation' as a title once. Later,
he passed a bust of Sheridan, looking young and tastefully
dishevelled. Dead and famous and another Honorary
Englishman. Beyond the final room, he found the cafe and a
very large pot of tea.

'What do you mean by that?'

'English writers. Like Naomi Mitchison, Alistair MacLean – they're Scottish writers, but they're never described that way. They are assumed to be English; good equals English.'

'Well, most folk have always known that and you could argue some cases either way. It's a bit of a red herring, really, not the central issue, and what does it have to do with my work? I was never well known enough to be Scots.'

'I wondered what you thought. I wondered if you'd ever thought of going South.'

'Instead of going West?'

He couldn't mistake it, she was laughing at him. He'd seen an odd light in her eyes before, but now she was almost giggling. In a way, it was nice to see, but now he couldn't tell if she honestly meant what she said.

'Look, David, I could have moved to England, to France, to America, the fact is, it wouldn't have worked. Nobody liked my work when I was in Scotland – don't look like that, I'm not feeling sorry for myself. I mean nobody liked it enough for me to live. I could not make a living. I always had to do other work in order to finance my writing when the other work meant that I barely had time to sleep. I wrote or worked and existed, that was all, and it wasn't worth it. I had to give up too much.

'And I couldn't move because I'm a Scottish writer. I don't mean that it's a betrayal to write elsewhere. I think it might have been, in my case, but that's not what I'm saying. The fact is that, disconnected from Scotland, I find I don't have much to write about. Scotland was my way in.

'And I get homesick.'

'But if you knew you would be homesick here and you knew you wouldn't be able to write... Why?'

'Because I don't care any more. I just don't care.'

It wasn't a good conversation to have as their first.

The rain had become a chill dust in the breeze as he found the right pond on the Green and stood in front of the sign with its painted ducks. His pause in the gallery seemed to have driven the damp against his skin. He was shivering.

Almost at once, he heard a call.

'Mr Reid, David Reid? Hello, there. Come over this side,

we'll go to Bewley's, have some tea. I should have thought it
would rain.'

He turned and saw her standing across the grey water.
Even at that distance, the blue of her eyes was obvious; strik-
ing, he thought. He waved, then paused for a moment before
he could make for the path. Seeing her there, it had seemed
quite possible he would step out onto the lake and then run
to meet her.

In the steamy warm of Bewley's with his second pot of tea,
he watched her eat a raisin muffin, slicing it carefully into four.
Sometimes she would lick her lips for crumbs and he noticed
her tongue was a very pale candy floss pink. Just to ease her
into talking, he outlined his Theory of the Honorary English.

'David, what do you expect from a colonised culture? The
better Scottish writing gets, the less it will matter. The work
will improve itself, it won't be competing with anything other
than the best it can produce. It will be international.'

'You sound quite passionate.'

'Perhaps I am.'

'But you don't want to write.'

'It isn't a question of wanting. There's no point.'

'You can't believe that.'

'Watch me.'

David didn't go back to his hotel, not straight away. He
had to walk. Monagh bent towards him when they parted,
but only shook his hand. No kiss. He didn't know how he
felt, except that he probably wanted to cry.

Monagh. Bitch. She was a disappointing bitch. A very
lovely, disappointing bitch.

It was dark and the rain was finished. As the sky cleared,
the wind grew colder and he noticed he could see the stars.
Looking up from the centre of Glasgow that wouldn't have
been possible, but the comparison didn't please him. Dublin
seemed to be the only capital that was uglier in the dark.
Maybe that wasn't fair, but away from O'Connell Street the
place seemed to pinch in and he wanted the nicotine and
whitewash Glasgow sky. He wished she hadn't talked about
being homesick.

What had happened to the woman? She only seemed to
come alive when she was saying that her talent had no point.

How could anyone enjoy just tearing their life up like that? She was almost gleeful.

If she thought *her* writing was pointless, then where on earth was he? Drip feeding a literary mirage with shitey free-lance journalism. He wasn't even a journalist, hadn't written a story in months. Bitch.

Tomorrow, he was invited to her house. That would have been wonderful. But now he didn't want to go. She wouldn't talk properly about writing, she was famously secretive about her private life, he had no idea why she wanted to see him again. He was mystified. And he had a piece to write about her. Did she know how hard he'd pushed to even get the chance to do it – a piece he really cared about? At the moment it would start with 'Where is she now?' and finish with 'fucking Dublin'.

The name of the pub escaped him. Quite probably, he never knew it. He drank Guinness which he didn't like and made him sick. No one sang or spoke Gaelic, nobody laughed a hearty, Irish laugh. The faces in the gantry glass confused him. They could have been in Glasgow, his breed; sharp and dispossessed. But this was their own, independent country now, they should be changed. They had their own money, their own army and they should be changed. They should be able to tell him how to change.

Finally flat in his hotel bed, David couldn't get warm. Between his head aching and the deep cold in his feet, he didn't think he slept at all until the morning. He missed breakfast.

Monagh's flat, at least, was a pleasant surprise. She had the second floor in a square Victorian house built of pale brick. The street could have been in any London suburb. He climbed a flight of concrete steps and rang at a door painted crimson to match the wooden shutters and window frames. Clearly, there were still some things Monagh managed to care about.

'Bless you.'

He sneezed almost as soon as she opened the door.

'I thought you were looking chilled yesterday. You should be careful.'

'Thanks, it's alright. I'm mainly tired.'

That sounded more bitter than he intended. Monagh seemed to glow, while he'd spent the night in mourning for the death of her career. Perhaps she really didn't care.

They had tea. More tea. Then.

'I should show you round. That's the kind of thing you want?'

'If you don't mind; that would be nice.'

She steered him along the hallway to the kitchen, a room he guessed would be sunny at the right time of the year. Her bedroom was almost empty. Single bed. The bathroom, too, was remarkably bare, not even an old leaf dropping from the ivy plant. David was about to ask her why she didn't seem to have any books when she opened a final door. Her Bluebeard room.

It was small and made smaller by ranks of shelves. In the window was a plain oak table beside a filing cabinet.

'It's a study.'

'That's right. My study has always been like this. I take it with me.'

'From Scotland?'

'Yes, everywhere. It makes me feel at home. Don't worry, I don't use it. It's here to remind me of my mistakes; so I won't make them again. You believe you can only really learn from your past?'

'Of course. But, you honestly don't ever go in here?'

'Only to dust.'

'You... I'm sorry, but you seem to like suffering. Why do you keep this here?'

When she didn't answer he thought she was offended, but she only smiled in the manner of certain religious pictures and offered him more tea.

It was dark by the time he left her and he still had almost nothing to put in his story. If he didn't get somewhere with her on Saturday, he would have to give up. A whole fortnight's holiday pissed away in Dublin. His first and only foreign assignment buggered, to coin a phrase. They wouldn't even offer him expenses.

On Friday, David made it down to breakfast and then returned to his room, threw up and went to bed. He felt fever-

ish. The morning and the afternoon shone through the curtains, modified by giant pink roses and their giant grey leaves
and he slept. The radio played through his dreams, adding the
day's news here and there while Monagh sat in her square,
bare living room and told him there was nothing he could do.

'Write yourself better, David. Alter the exchange rate, save
Kuwait. You want to be a writer; you believe in all of this.'

He tried to dream her onto her bed. Her hair would lie
against the crimson coverlet. Why did she like crimson so
much, when it always reminded him of blood? Her skin
would be on the crimson, pale as the belly of a hare. And...
and then they would be able to write. Together. They would
fuck and write and make things, it was all the same process.
She would be so nice on that coverlet, and then all wrapped
up in it later when he brought tea.

At three o'clock in the morning, David rang the night
porter and asked him for coffee, sandwiches. He ate and
drank quickly, very hungry, showered and made his bed.
When he woke again it was time for breakfast and fully
Saturday.

Monagh had baked them both biscuits.

'You can have another. There's no one else to eat them but
me.'

'Thanks, they're very nice.'

She allowed herself a smile and crossed her legs with a
nylon hiss.

'No need to sound quite so surprised.'

And Monagh smiled again, clattering the spoon as she put
down her cup. She smoothed the grey woollen dress taut over
her lap and glanced at the carpet, then the walls. When she
flicked a hand through her hair, David caught a snatch of her
perfume, clean skin and scented soap.

'Well, David, it's time to be very serious. I have something
to show you, come on.'

Her tension seemed to melt as she moved for the door,
pulling David up from the sofa by his hand. She tugged him
behind her, out along the passageway, and he felt a heavy
pulse start in his throat, felt his breath race, felt her fingers on
his palm.

Monagh opened the furthest door and left him to drift in
behind her. On the clean wood of her table, there was a nar-
row stack of foolscap sheets. She scooped it up and held it
out towards him, eyes terribly blue, lips parting.

'How much will you give me for it. You win, you get first
refusal. What am I bid?'

'I'm... Monagh. I... what do you mean?'

She smiled and dipped her head a touch to the side.

'David, it's what you were looking for; it's why you're
here. I thought somebody would come, eventually. Silly things
you think of when there's time on your hands.

'Please don't misunderstand me, David, I've given this up,
I have no interest in this. But I did think, if I was so popular,
so highly regarded – you said it yourself – I did think that
someone might have wondered where I'd gone, if I was still
writing, or if I had anything left behind unpublished.'

'Oh, I'm sure people wondered. I have. I've heard folk
saying, really.'

'Well, it took a fucking while for you to ask me. You,
plural.'

She sighed, almost too softly to be heard.

'This is my last story. When I finished it, there wasn't any
more. It stopped. That's the truth, I didn't stop it, it stopped
itself. There were leftovers, attempts and rewrites and then
nothing. I suppose my confidence had gone.'

'Your last story.'

'Yes. You can have it. I'll be perfectly honest with you, I
need the money. Any money.'

'That's very, very... thank you. I'll have to be honest with
you, too. I'm here to write an article about you, that is the
only reason that I'm here. But as soon as I get home, I'll talk
to people. They'll be very keen, I'm sure they will.'

Monagh returned the papers to the table without speaking, then sat with her back to the light. She would have sat
like this when she was typing.

'So you'll hawk it round then, will you? Out with the beg-
ging bowl.'

'Look, it's my fault, you misunderstood me. This is my
fault. I'll just leave you to think. Some more tea – I could
make some. I'll do that. Yes.'

He turned and hoped to hear her crying as he walked

along the hall. Crying would be good, a wee release. She'd prefer to do that privately and appreciate his tact.

'You see, David,'

She pulled his head round, made him stop before he knew what she had said.

'It does become quite important, after a while, that people ask you for your work. When you've been doing it for years, I mean for years; since I was your age; and the people who know have told you what a wonderful writer you are, you do just now and then, really want to be fucking asked.'

'Of course, I –'

'Don't say you understand. You do not understand. I'm not stupid, I worked very hard not to get my hopes up; just to write. But people say these things, you get reviews and you think you'll get work, at least something... I never had one offer of work in all those years. Not one.'

'Surely, there was something.'

'Never anything to do with writing – my writing. You end up doing nonsense; journalism, readings, anything, and folk think you're doing OK. They think you don't need to be asked. That's my problem, David, I never looked desperate enough.'

'But Monagh, if you were still able to work, if people liked what you did. Wasn't that enough?'

'No! It's not enough. I gave up too much for it ever to be enough. No one ever understood what I wrote, it never got any serious attention, it never changed anything. There just wasn't any point in doing it.'

'Monagh, please, come on and we'll go out. We'll have dinner.'

'Mr Reid, this is very sweet and I know you mean well. You seem a very nice young man, but please, just go away. You're too young to see this, you think you've got time to do better.'

'Oh for fuck's sake! You're so bloody self-obsessed. Do you know, you've talked about nobody else since I met you. Other writers are only there to be compared with you. Nobody else has it tough. You've got a house, you've got health, you've got your job, but you've got it tough.

'Why the Hell should we all be waiting for every word you write? Who do you think you are? Why should your stories be able to change the world? If you want us all to jump whenever you have an idea, you should be a military dictator. Why write?

'You had it all there for you. You could get inside people's heads, change them by showing them things they'd never thought of, make them happy. You could plant the seed and maybe it wouldn't grow now, but it would do later. Only you've gone in the huff. You just don't want to play any more. You need to be asked, you say? Well who fucking doesn't. You have an obligation to us and you've chickened out.'

He found he was shouting, leaning over the table and starting to sweat.

'I'm sorry, I've hurt your feelings. I'll go.'

'Not at all. I apologise for letting you down, Mr Reid. I find one's idols are never quite up to scratch.'

'No, you haven't let me down. It just seems such a waste, Monagh. I mean a waste of you.'

'I don't think there's all that much of me left, David. Don't fret.'

They had tea in the living room, very quietly, talking about Dublin and the places he should go to see. When she had fetched his hat and coat, Monagh sat beside him on the sofa.

'Do you think you'll write the article?'

'If you don't mind, I think I will. You know, it might make people ask you for work. It might not, though. I mean, I won't beg for you.'

'I know that. Look, take this, too.'

She had the manuscript in her hand.

'If anyone wants it, you can tell me. I refuse to be hopeful. But you might as well have it as not. That sounds very ungracious – I would like you to have it, David. There you are.'

Even out on the pavement, he could feel the pressure of her hand, through the paper. There was also the little weight of a kiss on his cheek.

'Bye, bye, David. No need to keep in touch. Unless something happens.'

And they parted with a doorstep kiss, perhaps like lovers.

David caught a flight to Glasgow on Monday afternoon. Sunday had been too grey to make another week of Dublin seem bearable. He knew, if he stayed, he would end up calling her. He knew he should refuse to be hopeful.

He walked out of Glasgow airport with his holdall unsearched, nothing he felt willing to declare. Somewhere between his shirts, he knew there was a sheaf of paper, just over a dozen pages, and he felt them tug his arm as he stepped. They carried a story called 'Warming My Hands and Telling Lies' which dealt with night-time disfigurements and invisible creatures called Industrialists. David worried it might be difficult to sell, but was happy to have it, as if he had suddenly met an old friend. A school friend. Only one thing had changed, now there was an introduction. Monagh must have added it later, or decided not to read it out one Friday afternoon, a very long time ago.

This story is as much as I can make it and must now speak for itself. Only you will know if it succeeds because I will stay here in the past and somewhere else.

My chosen title is a different case and does require additional explanation.

Once, out driving beside my second husband, I ran my fingers up his thigh. He asked me what I was doing.

'Just warming my hands.'

'Such lies.'

'Yes, I'm warming my hands and telling lies.'

You will recognise the relevant phrase.

As a year or two nudged past us, our relationship changed. My husband began to dislike me and then to hate. He hated my voice and my body, but perhaps most of all, he hated me to write.

'What are you doing"

'What do you think?'

'Up there fucking writing all day, you'd be better off having a wank. Who do you think ever actually reads all that shite?'

'You don't object when it earns us money.'

'Remind me when that was, it's so long ago. I earn enough for both of us. Why don't you try retiring – you could take up being a wife.'

One day when I was asked what I was doing I shouted back, 'Warming my hands and telling lies.'

I don't know why these words occurred to me, only that they seemed entirely true. I sat and typed out fabrications, keeping my hands snug and supple on the little, black keys. That was all it came to, nothing more. Just warming my hands and telling lies.

Norman Kreitman

A CATALOGUE OF THE POSSIBLE

There are those who can point their lives
to beyond what is possible. These are saints
who as in eclosis split their skins
and dry in the sun before ascending.
This is the musician who goes to live
between the notes of his symphony.
This the geneticist, gazing starstruck
at a firmament of ten thousand genes,
planning odysseys. And these fathers
sitting in parks, watching their childrens' future.
    All these are such as live
    forwards from the visible.

There are also those trapped by the impossible.
These are good women deluded by hopes of love,
half-admired by friends but left to perish.
These are fanatics who say no to the provisional,
want gardens yet no compromise of soil and sky.
This the psychotic, whose metaphors are irreversible,
whose meanings clicked shut and left him bewildered.
This is the sad one who combs his hair sideways
and looks in the mirror for a brave young man.
All these are such as are locked out
    and in ebbing years explore
    the geography of exile.

ON A LINE OF NORMAN MACCAIG'S

A square owl, sitting alone on his branch
is a chairman come early, awaiting his committee.
We exchange stares, and the bale of his amber eye
lambasts me for trespassing. So I drive on,
past the bank where the velvet bees
are quitting overtime at their foxglove mansions,
and as I leave the spinney the west
climbs through the open window like a sunset.
Below, Tweed with its honour-guard of lindens
moves backwards into the haze. The sky
is a pink and white theatre from high to horizon
sealing off the world, holding me in. So often
has this valley swathed me in images.

Yet I dislike all metaphors, their exactitude, irrelevance,
their gain and loss of sanity. Besides, at times
a man wants a bit of peace. It is good to be home,
be prosaic. I smile at you across the kitchen,
lightly touch your arm. Yet even here
pausing at the centre I'll secretly admit
that how I think and how I love depends
on pictures glimpsed and slipped again.
Wherever I stand I am travelling among valleys
and sloping woods, or some familiar fiction.

T. Lardans

WHAT'S SPEAKING?

Hello
   Hello, Hello

twelve inches, so
Hello
what do you like
           so
   doing
a number

     is Jim on the line
bring girls

  no, there
Hello
       dark
  dark, listen
call back at eight a.m.

a
  construction worker

  Hello
seriously

  no, Hull
      pierced
  and sellotaped
 have fun
my number, you want my number

  there then

Hello
friday so this line
  behind you
8537

  twelve inches, so
my wife will be out by then

  Hell, Hello

Brenda Leckie

ABYSSINIA

The walls are grey as clotted mist
and two feet thick. The builder of the house
fitted the stones together like a jigsaw.
You still can't see a chink
of daylight through them, but the roof
was scalped by gales long since.
'It's a good house, there's runnin' watter
in ivery room,' says Jim. Wee Maggie
groups us for a photy. Then we glance
into the but-and-ben, where ferns
grow on the hearth, and Jim
attempts a traverse of the gable-end.
A wind-bent rowan guards the door.
'Nae witches here,' says Ken,
grinning at Maggie and myself
shapeless in waterproofs, black hoods
over our dripping hair. Jim steps
from the ruined byre. We lift our packs
and leave. 'Ye know the place was built
by a man who could get nae work
so went to Abyssinia, a job
on the railway there. It's runnin' still,
I hear,' says Cal, easing his stride
as he plods on down the glen,
and turns to give one backward glance
at the stone-cold chimney-stacks
of Abyssinia, fading
into the low cloud.

NIGHT AND FOG

Waves crash
upon the roof. Somewhere
beyond the street
a troubled ocean flings
a tsunami at our coast.

We do not talk to those
who travel with us
(the silent crowds
gathering at entrances
to tube-stations.)

Instead, we hear
an unseen throng
of deep-sea mouths, that speak
with human tongues.

When darkness ebbs
we still avert our gaze
from passers-by, afraid
lest we or they acknowledge
what we heard.

Douglas Lipton

ANCIENT MAN PLOUGHING

Because he was dragging behind him
an oddly-formed piece of wood,
he claimed he was
an ancient man ploughing,
but all we saw
was a little bulbous boy
fetching firewood.

THE YELLOW JERSEY

Death is Jim in the yellow jersey
Jim from the passageway below
Jim who mounts the groaning rungs
and leans on you when you don't know.

So if you see the yellow glow
and hear him padding down below
don't even whisper from your loft.
Lie still and keep your breathing soft.

A GRANDCHILD SINGS

The wind always blows
and the snow never lies
and the sun only shines
for three weeks at a time
and the beaches are heavy with whales

and the sun never shines
and the wind never blows
and the snow always falls
for three weeks at a time
and the beaches are heavy with whales
and the air is bouncing with flies

and the trees never grow
and the grass is too green
there are shells in the river
and blood on the sand
and the beaches are heavy with whales
and the air is bouncing with flies
and my mouth is burning with water

and the clouds are too low
and the sky is too thin
and the earth is too thick
and the moon is too full
and the beaches are heavy with whales
and the air is bouncing with flies
and my mouth is burning with water
and the mildew is eating the buildings

and the parrots are black
and the worms are all white
and the dust in the drains
and the rust in the drawers
and the beaches are heavy with whales
and the air is bouncing with flies
and my mouth is burning with water
and the mildew is eating the buildings
and the windows are running with glass

the lights are all out
and the stars are all out
when the sun is not out
and when we are not out
and the beaches are heavy with whales
and the air is bouncing with flies
and my mouth is burning with water
and the mildew is eating the buildings
and the windows are running with glass
and the puppies are all growing teats

and the people are old
and the money is gone
the walls are all down
and the dominoes done
and the beaches are heavy with whales
and the air is bouncing with flies
and my mouth is burning with water
and the mildew is eating the buildings
and the windows are running with glass
and the puppies are all growing teats
and Dolly is crying real tears
and Dolly is having a baby.

Linda McCann

TOM LEONARD'S GOOD NIGHT

Mr Greeting-Face, Mr Testy,
Mr World's-Weight-on-Shoulders.
Unanimous hands lift and push,
Submerge him into a black taxi,
Shut the door along with him.
Like a cork, up he bobs again
Stuck half-through the window,
Telling us another thing.
I hug him, shout 'I love you Tom.'
The taxi moves. He watches me,
Near-sober, lost for abuse. Roars
'I don't fuckin deserve it then.'

LATE PARENTHOOD

What does c'est juste mean?

Eh, sensuous is when
a woman is all
provocative and
flirting...

Well it's when
a man takes advantage of
a young girl
because she's
innocent and he
has his way with her...

(a pause)

No. C'est juste.

I don't know.

I don't know.
Is it French?

Mary McCann

APRICOT SLICE IN THE PEOPLE'S PALACE

it's raining cats and dogs
it's queuing pensioners
it's pizzicato on the roof
it's tea and apricot slice and a smile
carried joyfully to a damp bench
under palms that ambush me
with inflated raindrops

it's you arriving, damp and scattered
and me with my cup filled to overflowing and
I press you to an apricot slice
a slab of orange happiness
and tart delight

we share a bench like two pigeons in winter
and watch an old man drawing

and a wedding party enters, pink and white
with sober suits and cameras
for photos among ferns, and palms, in Paradise

paradise palms, the Winter Gardens
tasting of apricots, and you beside me
a palace in Glasgow in the rain

MULTISTOREY

that light in the sky –
someone's kitchen!
someone is happy behind
these orange, those pink
several red – curtains!
someone has supper in the air
someone is hoovering
the fifteenth floor!
someone sleeps behind
grey blue squares
someone is crying their eyes out
to the TV
someone thinks, in green

the lift staggers creaking
from floor to floor
like a steel mole
someone deserves better

like a vertical ship with square portholes
the tower looms into the dark
dizzy on the ground, I stare up
someone's lit windows look like home

you are up there, my love
playing the piano in the sky!

DOUBLE TAKES IN SHOPPING CENTRE

excuse me madam
I thought you were a mannequin
stock still – but
your clothes are grey
not buttercup or turquoise
your poise is short lived
I see you are human
just a customer, like me

sorry sir
for a minute I thought you were walking on the ceiling
scientist solves antigravity I presume
boost for local superstore
but I see you are only a reflection
in our superior supermarket wraparound
wall to wall mirrors

pardon
I thought this was a shopping trolley
but I see it has gashed a person on the ankle
what can you trust these days

excuse me madam
I thought you were a shopper
but I see I am having a brush
with a floor cleaner
I apologise for disturbing your rubbish
the floors here are a miracle really
such a shine on a shoe string
and the minimum rate per hour

I'm sorry ladies
I thought you were running for fun
but I fear you are shoplifting, for that
heavy man with the walkie talkie has stopped you
and I see you are desperate

excuse me sir I thought you were a human being
but I see you are a security guard
I thought I was a law abiding citizen
but I am afraid I am angry

I see I must keep my nose clean
and my hands off the buttercup blouses
or I too will be hustled through the looking glass
into a hidey hole behind the off licence
where nothing is what it seems

what the eye doesn't see
the heart still grieves for

James McGonigal

THE BLIND

Runs like a Chinese monkey up the fraying cord
of its own tail and hangs there squint:
one lazy lid above the window's startled blue
or browned off grey or red rimmed glance at dawn.
Our breath all winter wept behind its slats

that fall like unpinned hair at close of day.
The orange sky of evening never dies:
Glasgow sparks and skids on heavy lids
as we enter the room with one last half cup
cooling in our hands.

You've gone on up ahead tonight. East winds are
working late and so am I. Stuffed into corners
dry leaves make duvets for hedgehog and shrew.
Advent will iron them stiff linen covers.
We hoped to dream through it.

That river of filth lapping the doorstep last night
me breasting its waves and suddenly finding
a standpipe of fresh to rinse my sticky skin –
Waking to roll it all up in the blind's dry
bedmat of rushes. Stashed it away.

You're miles from me already. Hearing your breath
in the half dark I pull on night clothes,
star jacket and baggy cloud trousers,
to follow you into the sky of sleep.
I saw eternity: the other night

wrapping each body in its sheets of light.

POSTING

Grey trees whose lungs had filled up with winter
suddenly exhaled a breath of leaves –

You caught the dawn train south. The power stack
was already pointing its beam of smoke

straight in the morning's face. Houses held up
chilled hands to the sun: plum-coloured light

glowed through their nails and entered the room
where we had dipped our fingers

in the same dish of hours. Beside the gate
a little bush was shouldering its weight

of blossom and seemed about to stagger up the path
and post a lifetime's letters, one by one,

onto the tiles behind the locked storm doors.

EYE OF THE BEHOLDER

The garden pool's eye glazes
in a dream of evaporation: help I'm expiring
fern stems and sun's lips sucking
my water-skin tighter

quick fill me with tears – bucketfuls
of the shocking drops between lashes of bulrush.
Everything clouds, clears: three goldfish
gleam in a pupil appraising the blue

and in their midst, with dripping basin, you.

Duncan McLean

FIRE, BLOOD, WINE

We were working on a site near the old Leith canal. Half a street of warehouses had been demolished a couple of years before, but it was only now that anything was being done with the land. We'd been sent there before anyone else, old Carl, me, and the new YTS. Her name was Chris and she knew nothing about the job. Or at least she wasn't letting on that she knew anything. In fact she wasn't saying much at all, so Carl had plenty of time to yap away; Chris wasn't interrupting – maybe she wasn't even listening – and I was having to do most of the work.

See what he's doing now? Carl said. He's cleared a space there, kicked the bricks out of the road, trampled down the weeds and that, and now he's putting up the structure, the skeleton of the thing. Three decent timbers, that's all you need: good thick branches if you're in the parks, or sleepers maybe if you're by the railway, or like here we've just looked around and found this old door, and we've got out the hatchet and took out three of these good thick planks.

I paused in smashing up an ancient tea chest. *I* looked around, I said, *I* got out the hatchet.

What's he doing now? said Carl.

Chris shrugged.

I'm working, I said, Do you mind what that is Carl?

What you have to do next is get a good substructure, a kind of heart to the thing inside the main frame there. Smaller bits of wood or board, big bits of the right kind of rubbish, a tyre or two, cardboard boxes maybe if you fold them down...

I walked up and stuffed an armful of crumpled newspaper and assorted crap into the middle.

See? said Carl, Just about anything can go in at this stage, anything as long as it burns.

Aye, but you have to be careful with some things, I said. Some of the furniture you find, old settees and that, you have to watch out for the fumes they give off, stand upwind, ken, well upwind.

I glanced at the girl to see if she was taking it all in. She was staring at her boots. I looked over at Carl, and he looked back. He took his pipe out of his pocket and tapped it against his leg, then gazed into the bowl and poked around in it with his pinkie.

Away and show her where the petrol is, he said.

I sniffed. Are you sure the strain won't fucking kill her?

He looked up. Watch your language in front of the lassie, he said.

For fuck's sake Carl, I said, I never asked to have a lassie put on with us! It's those cunts up in city chambers who're to blame for that. Why should I change my way of talking all of a sudden? I'll talk how I fucking like. Christ, you're so worried about the girl... I haven't heard *her* fucking complaining!

You haven't exactly been fucking listening, have you?

Both of us looked at her in amazement. It was just about the first thing she'd said all morning. Carl started to say something, but she carried on speaking over him.

I am fucking complaining, she said. I'm fucking fed up of yous calling me a lassie, going on about mind the girl and all that: I'm not a fucking girl!

There was a pause. You could've fooled me, I said.

I'm seventeen years old, she said, I'm a fucking woman!

Carl chuckled, stuck his pipe in his mouth. Oh aye hen, he said. Right enough. Sorry.

I started to walk off towards the van. Come on then woman, I called back, Come and give us a hand with this petrol. She didn't come after me.

Five minutes later, I'd poured a measure of petrol into the base of the structure, and splashed some over the sides and top too.

Carl cleared his throat. Stand back! he said. I looked at him. We'd been working together for three years, and he'd never said stand back before. Since when did he tell me what to do? I took a pace away anyhow. I always did, it was common sense. The girl stepped back too. Carl nodded at me, then at her. He struck a match and lifted it in cupped hands to the bowl of his pipe, hunched over slightly till he worked on that and got it going, then, just before the match burnt out, he threw it into the base of the fire, almost without looking, as if it didn't matter, like he was just chucking it away, and in an instant the whole structure streaked into flames.

Carl had jumped away the moment he'd dropped the match. Now he settled down on his hunkers, gazing at the fire, watching how it was going. I took a few steps round the far side to check it was burning evenly, then went over and stood beside him. Chris came over too.

See how the orange flames are dying down now? said Carl. That's the petrol burnt out. But there's others coming through, red and yellow and bits of blue and that: that's the wood and stuff catching. This is the important time. If the fire's going to take it takes now.

We all looked at the fire. It was doing fine.

If the heart's too tightly packed the flames don't catch, I said. On the other hand, if the insides are too loose they'll blaze up and be ashes in half a minute, and still you'll be left with the bones of the thing standing there.

I looked over at Carl and the girl. He was ricking on his pipe, she was holding her hands out to the heat.

But it looks like I put it together pretty fucking well, I said. There was a pause.

So what do we do now? said Chris.

Well... we just watch this one for a while, said Carl, Feed it up a bit. Then it might well be dinnertime. Then this afternoon we're away down to the docks.

What is it there the day? I said, A skip?

Carl took his pipe out of his moth, shook his head. Line says three oil drums.

Drums of oil? said Chris.

I doubt it, said Carl. They're meant to take oil and chemicals and that away to some furnace somewhere.

But it wouldn't be the first time they haven't, I said.

Carl knocked his pipe out on the ground, then brought it up to his mouth and blew through the stem. Aye Chris, he said, That's one thing about this job: you start a lot of different kinds of fires.

Different fires for different folks, I said.

The girl looked over at me. Her face was blank.

At dinnertime Carl sat in the van as usual, eating his sandwiches and listening to classical music on the radio. I remembered from when we'd been in this part of the world before that there was a good cafe closeby, so I headed off for that. As I reached the top of the steps from the canalbank to streetlevel, I heard somebody running up behind me. It was Chris. I kept on walking. Twenty yards down the street she caught up with me, then for half a block she walked along two paces behind me, till I stopped.

Is this it? she said.

Oh, are you coming with me are you?

Well nobody told me I would need sandwiches. I mean I thought I'd be close enough to home to...

Look, if you're coming with me, come with me; don't hang around my arse like a... like a bad fucking penny.

She looked at me for a second, and I thought she was going to greet, but all of a sudden she burst out laughing. You really hate me, don't you? she said, then started laughing again.

Christ, I'm just needing my dinner, I said, Is that so fucking much to ask?

She started walking again, and so did I. Okay, she said, Where is this cafe?

Just across there, I said, and nodded to the other side of the street.

Where?

That red place, I said, With the steamy window.

I thought that was a sauna. Could they not afford a sign or something?

Fuck knows. Why don't you ask them if you're so interested.

Okay, I will.

Don't.

We went in. It was just like somebody's front room, except four kitchen tables had been crammed in, and there was a serving hatch across a door in the far side. Three of the tables were more or less full, and everybody glanced up as I came in and threaded my way over towards the hatch. I heard the door shut with a bit of a bang, then suddenly there was total silence, everybody stopped talking and eating and stared at Chris as she crossed the cafe behind me. All men. Fuck. Obviously it wasn't the done thing to bring females into the place. They'd be blaming me for the intrusion as well. I was beginning to wish I'd never mentioned the cafe to her, and wondering if I could just turn round and walk straight out.

Then I thought, Fuck it, where else am I going to get my dinner?

A middle aged woman with a big bosom and a big belly under her housecoat came over towards the serving hatch from the depths of the room behind it. Now son? she said.

What've you got?

We've got a menu. She leaned through the hatch and pointed to a paper plate pinned to the wall. It had writing on it in felt pen: BEEF STEW 90p, COD £1, RHUBARB CRUM-BLE 50p.

I'll have the stew, I said, And a mug of tea and the crumble as well.

Custard or milk?

Custard with the crumble, milk with the tea.

She jerked her head back, half closed her eyes and looked me up and down, then let out a loud hoot. I stared at her. She hooted again. It was laughter, I hadn't recognised it for a minute.

Give us a shout when it's ready, I said.

Hooh!

I turned and squeezed back across the room. As I was sitting down at the free table, I heard Chris talking over at the hatch: Have you nothing vegetarian?

Once again, all conversation in the cafe stopped.

I'll have the fish then, said Chris.

Somebody whistled. A few folk looked over at me. I picked something up from the table. It was an old pepsi bottle that had been filled up with sauce. I unscrewed the top, then picked some dried brown stuff out of the thread with my fork. Chris sat down on the bench opposite me. I put the bottle down.

So you're a veggie are you? I said. She shrugged. So is cod a vegetable then? She looked at me. I smiled. She looked away. So what do you reckon so far? The job I mean...

Is there a bog? she said.

What? I leant towards her.

She cleared her throat. A bog, she said loudly, Is there a toilet in here?

Christ's sake, no, I said. What do you think this is, the fucking Ritz?

There must be a bog, otherwise where does the old woman

go when she needs a pish?

Don't ask me. Maybe she does it in the fucking stew for all I know.

I'm going to ask her.

Oh fuck.

Chris went over to the serving hatch and leaned over it, saying something to the woman in the back. After a few seconds, she lifted the counter and walked through. There was a general shaking of heads and complaining, then everybody went back to eating or what they were talking about before.

At one table somebody was saying, I heard of a woman who fed her man Kittikat and chips for tea one night, and he died.

Shite man!

It's true enough.

Kittikat wouldn't kill you!

Och, the cat food didn't kill him; he broke his neck when he bent down to lick his arse!

STEW!

The woman was shouting from the hatch. I got up and went over. As I lifted the plate off the counter, she said, Oi, here's the fish for your dame as well.

She's not my...

Before I could finish, another door in the back room opened, there was the sound of a cistern filling, and Chris stepped out with a big grin on her face. When she saw me at the hatch, she threw her arms up in the air and shouted, Yeaahhh! I've got my chatties! No more abortions for me!

The cafe behind me went quiet, but for some reason this time I wasn't worried. I was standing there, a plate of stew and peas in one hand, fish and chips in the other, watching Chris dance around the backshop, shaking her hips, throwing her hands in the air, shouting and laughing. And I couldn't help myself, I was laughing too. I laughed till I got jabbing pains in my sides and I had to put the plates down for fear of dropping the lot.

You're a daft cow, I said, in a gap in my laughter.

She put her hands up to her ears like horns, and started prancing about making mooing noises.

The woman who ran the place was laughing too. I'd kill for a glass of what she's on, she said.

Come on Chris, I said, Come and get your grub before it's time for work again.

She looked over at me, grinning. Fuck work! she said.

We ate quickly, not speaking, then I took the plates up to the counter, told the woman not to bother about the crumble, paid, and made for the door. Chris was waiting outside. As I came out, she started walking further up the street. I followed her.

They'll be talking about us for weeks in there, I said.

Ach, who cares! she said, striding on ahead.

Eh, where are we going?

She stopped in front of a paki shop. Well, is this place licensed?

I pressed my face against the window and looked in. There's cans on a shelf there.

Right, wait here.

Half a minute later she came out with a big green bottle, and led back the way we'd come.

What's that?

Sherry.

Sherry?

Aye, this is a celebration.

How can we celebrate? We've got to start work again in fifteen minutes...

Forget it! if you're so worried about the time, stop talking and start drinking.

She made to pass the bottle, then took it back, unscrewed the top, and put it in her jacket pocket. She took a quick drink, then handed me the sherry. As the bottle was in my mouth, she spoke again.

I owe you a quid for dinner, right? Well the wine was one-eighty, so if we more or less halver it, that's us squared up, okay?

I held the bottle out to her, wiped my mouth on my sleeve, and was away to say something, but already she'd taken a swig and was talking again.

Christ, who wants a kid, eh? Who'd bring one into this world? Not me, anyhow. I mean, do you ken what this government's done to family allowance? Bastards! It's fucking atrocious, ask anyone, ask my mum. She took a quick drink,

YIPPEE! she shouted.

We went down the same steps we'd come up earlier. When she got to the canalbank, Chris turned right and walked in the opposite direction to where the van was parked. I followed her. A few yards on, she sat down under a tree, balanced the bottle on a rock by her side, then got out a packet of Marlboro and lit up.

I never knew you smoked, I said. You never lit up all morning.

I thought I was pregnant, didn't I. She exhaled. Sit down and shut up.

I sat down. Already the two or three drinks of sherry were making me a bit unsteady. I leaned against the treetrunk as I went down, but once sitting I felt fine again, and lifted the bottle to take a drink. I looked at Chris as I was drinking. She was smiling, and blowing smoke out between her lips in a long jet.

I was beginning to worry this morning to be honest, I said. I mean I thought me and Carl had got stuck with a right miserable bitch – you hardly opened your mouth! – so, christ, it's a relief to find out it was just the old PMT...

She turned slowly to look at me. What? she said quietly.

Well it affects lots of dames like that, eh no? Makes them a bit depressed, a bit weepy and that. Christ, I sympathise, I mean cutting yourself shaving's bad enough, but all that buckets of blood? Yous are welcome to it!

You ignorant bastard! She snatched the bottle out of my hand.

What? I said.

I wasn't prefuckingmenstrual, I was worried in case I was going to be bringing a bairn into a world full of arseholes like you! Jesus, is that any reason to be cheerful?

She got to her feet and started walking straight for the canal. I jumped up, staggered slightly and fell back against the tree, then pushed myself upright and went after her. She'd stopped at the edge and was looking down past her feet into the dark, thick water. The bottle, still quarter full, dangled from her right hand. I stood slightly behind her, and to one side.

Don't do it, I said.

I'm going to.

Don't.

She bent the top half of her body back the way, then snapped it forwards, at the same time bringing her arm up and letting go of the bottle. It flew out over the canal and smacked into the water half way across, bobbed up once, then went under.

A few bubbles came to the surface. I watched them float off downstream. A tune came into my head. It was going round and round. I started to sing it: Come on baby light my fire, come on baby light my fire...

Chris took a step back from the edge and turned to face me. Is that supposed to be funny? she said.

What? I said. Is what supposed to be funny?

She was staring at me. I smiled. She looked beyond me, and nodded to where the van was parked.

Come on, she said, Let's get to work. I feel like burning a whole load of things.

118

John Maley

MADDER THAN HAMLET

To muse, perchance to cruise in loos.
You are too long i' the shit, m'lord,
madder than Hamlet, or the ghost of
Christmas camp, prejudice like poison
stinging in my ears, the penetration in
awkward arras is not what it appears.
I say that cloud's like a cock, a bag
of chips, nay, it is a man's lusty lips
longing to be kissed, out of my way I
say, I am at the mercy of your hips.
Will I be found floating in the Forth
and Clyde canal, hey nonny bloody no,
with fragrant flowers in my hair? I'm
fucked if bonny Scotland would care.

THE THATCHER YEARS

I

Stony rubbish, cruel months, fallen estates,
Possil, Gorbals, Drumchapel, Easterhouse,
Blackhill, heaps of broken images. Tiresias,
social worker in a combat jacket, gropes
blind in ugly closemouths, violent hours,
tumbling towerblocks, the battle scenes
perceived, foretells the rest with scribbled
case reports. Unreal City, between the giro
and the supersnoopers falls the shadow,
the pusher and the loan shark, the dead trees
that give no shelter twit jug twit jug.
Memories, desires, madly mix. Sweet Clyde,
run softly till I end my song, Sweet Clyde,
run softly, for I speak not loud or long.

II

The chair she sat in, like a burnt throne,
war words, her strange synthetic perfumes,
her red hair brushed out in fiery points.
Those are pearls that were her eyes. Fear
death by poverty, by the barbarous queen
so rudely forced. Do you know nothing? Do
you see nothing? Do you remember nothing?
'I remember all the streets savagely still,
Victorian family, solvent, virginal, around
the grand piano of the golden age empire.'
The fragments she has shored against her
ruin. Where the dead men lost their bones
she descends in a helicopter and still
she cries 'Jug jug' to shell-shocked ears.

III

The jobs have departed, leaving no addresses.
By the waters of the Clyde I sat down, wept
with all the gallus gluesniffers, hopeless, high,
heroin's heart beating a cool fool's retreat.
It riots and reigns in the junkie jungleland.
I had not thought smack had undone so many.
Unreal City, O City City I can sometimes hear
ancestral death-cries, Antony falling on his
sword, the pain of the hard man's poor wife.
This music crept by me upon the waters, left
me in the sweat of blood and tears, carried
through many vandalized halls, inexplicable
splendour, orange, green, white, gold, glisten.
In the DSS I can connect nothing with nothing.

IV

The burning burning burning burning middens
smoke me, choke me. Agonies in stony places.
A jessie rattles in a locked closet, done in.
That dream you planted last year in your
heart, has it begun to sprout? Will it bloom
this year? The wisest woman in all of Europe
deals her deadly pack, murderous jokers, open
season. Death on the rock. Bullets and gags.
You! Hypocrite with weird justice, odd peace
smelling of blood, tasting of fear. All profit
and loss, poor ends in the filthy whirlpool.
Suffer us not to mock ourselves with false
hood, a thousand nightmare launches. Lady, ten
Irishmen starved under your cruel iron rule.

V

After the coalmine black on sweaty faces,
after the echoes of plastic bullets that
ring in children's skulls, after the baton
charges, we who were living are now dying.
Who are those hooded hordes swarming over
endless streets, arid plains, with molotov
cocktails in the days of rage? Broadwater
Farm, Brixton, Belfast. The red sullen faces
sneer and snarl behind centurion shields.
Dixon of Dock Green with heavy truncheon.
O Lord thou fuckest me, crying 'You are here
to kneel.' Your creed's as cold as a slum's
pensioners in winter. I sat upon the shore
musing upon this thing my country's wreck.

Linda Marquart

DUCKS IN A ROW

Representations of ducks, not horses, marched up and down the walls of Elizabeth's room. Jemima Puddleduck and her ducklings enjoyed a perpetual tea-party.

A bit of wallpaper, imperfectly trimmed, stuck out from behind the plate covering the light switch. The young dog Jack followed Karen as she fetched the Exacto knife from her desk in the study and returned to the nursery to clip off the protruding shred of wallpaper. Using the tip of the blade, she tucked the remaining bit under the plate. She peered at the repair closely.

Satisfied, she looked once more around the room and went into the hall, closing the door behind her. The dog padded after her.

In the kitchen, she made a cup of tea. She glanced at the clock. Almost 4:30. Her mother would be on the telephone on the dot.

Karen put two chocolate biscuits on a plate to have with her tea. The dog whined softly and offered a paw. 'You'll have to wait for your lord and master, Jackie. He'll give you a game and a biscuit.' She leaned over as far as she could and caressed the animal's soft muzzle as he pushed his head into her palm. 'Biscuits aren't good for you, baby.'

Karen placed her hands on the counter and pushed herself upright from her bent-over position. Panting a little, she smiled and patted her eight-month's pregnant belly.

The telephone rang as she sat down with her tea.

The daily reassurances that her mother demanded were Karen's triumph. Each afternoon at 4:30 she was put on trial for having a baby at the age of thirty-eight, just as she had been put on trial before the age of thirty-eight for not having one.

'You're just selfish, that's what you are.' It had begun when Karen turned thirty. 'Both of you. You think that you're waiting until the time is right to have a child? You're just fooling yourselves. You want the money and the successes, the two careers, the two houses, skiing in the Alps, your aerobics classes.' Her mother's voice rose in pitch and emphasis as she worked down the list. 'The time will never be right, because you'll never be willing to give up your freedom. Or your control.' Karen, a deft mimic, used to repeat the tirades word for word to James, and they would both laugh.

Karen held the telephone away from her mouth as her mother talked. She nibbled a biscuit, one of two she allowed herself each day. Jack looked longingly at the biscuit.

Now every afternoon at 4:30 the lives that she and James had invented were vindicated. Karen had planned each step, each phase, each purchase, to dovetail and to be fulfilled at the moment of Elizabeth's birth. Her very career, chosen for the freedom that it would afford her and now interrupted for six months, consisted of solving the sorts of crises that she herself would never have allowed to happen at all.

The amniocentisis that had shown the baby to be a girl had also proven her triumphantly normal. In the nursery, all was in readiness, from the furniture to the nappies folded in the drawer. Answering her mother's question about her pregnancy gave Karen a sense of satisfaction almost as deep as that of the pregnancy itself. The two women said good-bye and Karen put the telephone down with a sigh.

Jack recognised the sound of James' car on the gravel drive before Karen even heard it. He was on his feet instantly, running to the door. Karen pushed herself out of the chair.

'Heigh-ho, Jackie.' James gave Karen a quick kiss and handed her the white bag from Marks & Spencer. He slung his briefcase on the floor and began to wrestle with the animal, pushing him away as the excited dog bounded towards him. The dog barked gleefully at his master, front paws extended on the floor, haunches in the air as he waited for the next joyous onslaught from the man.

James threw off his overcoat and dangled one of his leather gloves at the dog, holding it tantalizingly just beyond his reach, then flicking it away as Jack jumped for it, his jaws snapping shut on the empty air.

Karen watched from the doorway of the kitchen at the end of the long hallway. 'James, please don't tease him like that. It'll make him vicious. Please, dear.'

James did not hear Karen's exact words over the barking of the dog. 'Don't worry so much. It's only a game, Karen. We both know that, don't we, Jackie?' James shouted over the noise of the dog's furious barking. 'Do we have a chocolate biscuit for my friend?'

Karen was putting the chicken into the microwave oven. James followed her into the kitchen, still holding the glove out to the dog and shaking it at him. Karen gritted her teeth as the animal's barking filled the room. James took a chocolate biscuit from the tin and began to play the game using the biscuit instead of the glove to rouse Jack even further. The dog grew more and more frantic, leaping for the biscuit and snapping the air as James snatched it away.

Karen crushed the empty cardboard container in her hands and said evenly, 'James, don't tease him. It's so bad for him You mustn't teach him to do that. Please, James.' The dog's furious barking covered her words, and James, caught up in the game, laughing, continued to whirl the biscuit round and round in the air as Jack leapt and snapped and barked. The dog stopped for a moment, whining in his desire and despair. He looked into his master's face for the answer to his confusion. Then he began to bark and leap once more.

Karen forced herself to walk out of the kitchen and down the hall into the nursery. James's voice, barely audible over the barking, followed her. 'Darling, it's just a game.'

Karen closed the door of the nursery to block out the noise of Jack's barking. She eased herself into the rocking chair. The genteel orderliness of Jemima Puddleduck's tea-party mocked her. Karen circled her belly in her arms and wept.

Angus Martin

THE BURIED

I wonder how many people
are buried in Kintyre without
a memorial of any kind
over them, and if the lack
would matter to some of them
were they able to take a step
out of time and look at the ground
containing their dust but no
label of contents.

I know this: there are more people
unmarked than marked through millenia
of inhumations, but where exactly are they all
and what do they look like now?
Mostly they look like the earth itself,
and perhaps the potatoes or carrots
you ate today contained
infinitesimally the physical residue
of a flint-knapper
or a Pict who was cut down
under a still and blood-red sky
when the thousand-miles-travelled rollers
beat the drum of their own extinction
on the bay of Machrihanish
and sent a tribute of salt
into the swamplands of Laggan.

But don't stop eating potatoes and carrots –
there may be brains inside roots and tubers,
and perhaps a grain of another style
of experience will enter your chemistry
and on a screen in the dream-
laboratory you will watch
a flint nodule in the slowed-down
process of disintegration,
and, immediately after,
a sword will chop 'you' into bits
and you won't ever know which
were the flakes of the nodule
and which were the flakes of you.

BELOW ZERO

When Campbell was going home
by the moor way to his shepherd's hut,
swaggering and drunk from the fair,
and haranguing a deaf audience
of frost-glittering stars,
his fuddled senses failed him.

He did not know that Death
was on his trail, and caught him
on the mountainside, saying:
'Here – you're mine now:
let me dust this white stuff
over you while you sleep.'

Gordon Meade

THE LEWIS CHESSMEN

On Uig Sands I see
the game of chess
being played out
in my mind –

a rook stands
on the cliffs at
Crowlista and watches the waves
breaking on the sands
beneath him,

a bishop walks
the sands from Carnish
in the south-west to Timsgarry
in the north-east towards
the burial grounds,

a knight leaps
from rockpool to rock
pool his armour rusted
his knees skinned,

the king hides
in the dunes praying
to the shadow of the cross
his sword's hilt makes
on the sand,

and the queen sits
kneeling at the edge
of the ocean letting the waves
break over her unable
to be drowned.

Gus Morrison

FORMS OF APPLICATION

I am fed up tae the back teeth of filling forms wi spaces
asking for details of everything aboot me like dates of
when wis ye born and when will ye die and what colour
dae ye pee and how often dae yir bowels move and where
dae ye live and how dae ye live and dae ye break wind as
often as ye might, and dae ye think o' the moon and stars
when yir in yir bed at night and what dae ye think when yir
sitting on the pan is it totties and mince or strawberry jam
and what jobs huv ye hud and ye've nae right tae leave
them when there's millions and trillions like ye who canny
find a job daeing anything at aw and why dae ye want this
job is the daftest of them all – cos there already is a Prime
Minister ya fucking eejit – then, efter waiting for ages a
wee slip of paper comes back frae some stranger who has
read yir form and knows everything aboot ye even though
you know eff all aboot them and it says sorry pal but yir
bums oot the windae cos ma pals goat the job cos he's in
the Masons or the Labour Party or the hen-toed club or the
Rechabites or the blue light mob or some other farting
thing – then ye get mad at yirself for no telling them where
tae stick their form in the first place and ye wish ye were
wee again and ye wid pit Baldy Bain for yir name and huv
an address in another galaxy frae a planet that eats
earthlings who think up forms and rifts them into orbit.

Jobs for our boys

The deafening silence of solitude echoes through these walls
causing a pregnant pause to last forever until a child's
roar for mother gives a temporary respite to the unemployed
millions who if they could afford a newspaper of better quality
would find out that they are one of the most serious problems
today in the whole world and not just a local infliction on the
social security office where they spend their time when not
perambulating around their country on their two wheelers
taking the advice of their leader who knows that there
are new vacancies everyday if only they would raise
their lazy buttocks from the comfort of the home
and frequent the highways and byways of this
once great country of ours where everyone
has an equal opportunity regardless of
skin pigmentation or religion or what
school tie you wear when attending
interviews for jobs in the civil
service or the army where you
can carve out a future for
yourself and family and
patrol city streets in
Ulster hoping that
nobody fires any
bullets in your
direction.

John Murray

THE MEENISTER'S CAT

the new inductit young meenister
in her new manse study
screivin the sunday sermon
a gless muscadet aside inspirin texts
bane dry, caller an white
keeks doon an smiles upon her cat
whae curious tae see her wark saw late at een
wimples in atween warm limbs
an purrs sae deip an kirkielike
an sib untae an organ peep
that she blesses him
fae deip inwith her hert

fer the meenister's cat wis an angelic cat
beatific, chaste an decorous
evangelic an faithfu
guid an hummle yet infinite an joyous
the meenister's cat wis a kosher cat
leal, meek an noble
ossianic, pure an quintessential
rarified an sublime
the meenister's cat wis a transcendental cat
universal, virtuous an worshipfu
baith xenophyllic an zealous
een as he ZZZZZZZZZZZZZZZZZZZZZZZZed
dreamin on spuggies an meece
he wizzzzz

th'aul din meenister man
plankit his lane ben the victorian bing
he cudnae cry his ain
drafty an stoorie an as guddled as a Kafka castle
thinks on sermons past
that he can resurrect athoot yerkin
his elders fae their doucie dwams,

tae yaise as a closin text
afore he caas a curtain
ower his lang career,
an as he gethers the menses yet his
tae gar the daurk an daurkenin dram
tae his dry an drucken lips
aul baudrons smools thro wuiden legs
wi liftit tail an rig bane bou'd
narries its sleekit een
an commends his sowel tae hell
sssssssssssssssssssssssssssssssssssssscraichin

fer the meenister's cat wis an aetheist,
a bastard cat an a calvinist
baith diabolical an dour
evil, fushonless an grim
the meenister's cat wis a harem cat
iconoclastic an but a Jezebel,
Judas an Janus
forby a kelpie's cat
baith lewd an libidinous
the meenister's cat wis a malagrugous nihilist
obsequious an perverted
querulous, randy an satanic
thrawn, ugsome, vengefu an wicked
the meenister's cat wis an X certificate cat
ootae some zombie film
that ZZZZZZZZZZZZZZZZZZZZZZPAT at him
whae wis meenister

syne suddent wis dumstrucken
bi a fowertie oonse bottle
wheechin thro the air
sib untae a tongue of flame
writ large athort the lift
wappin it right atween the een
sae that it kythed a kittlin again
an the meenister spak furth sayin
that'll suffer the bugger tae cam untae me.

Thom Nairn

MISSING

Darkness
Heavy and wide as silence.
The mirrors interface slyly,
Walls clear with light,
A dream of dawn
Swept clean.

In city parks
Leaves shuffle up to the brush,
Itself dead wood.
Death on death
Makes the rush of a living sea.

Animal eyes and touch,
Slow steps wandering:
So many things are just a long walk
Around so much motion,
Turmoil.

When traffic moves like slush,
Snow around an anvil's neck,
Cities are just lizards,
Can't shake off their tails.

Autumn comes down as a shell
And trees go out like lights.

In a night without landscape
Dreaming of driven moons,
Chasing lost rooms and lives
That have become something different,
Something warm and wild
In a different constellation.

ABBEYMOUNT '91

Peering sleepily, curiously
In a shop-window.

It's a new one and I'm wondering
About samosa,
Pornography and potato puffs.
Yes. They sell wine.

A not so old man
Is buying three rolls,
Carefully:

Tea-bags
And some cheese
And some Grouse.

His eyes are moon craters,
His beard
A grey sea-matted tangle,
Struggling down over his chest.

He comes out as I'm still
Not quite there,
Lost on the edge
Of my own, unconscious, stare.

The eyes have a hurt in them
But smile wide
At their deep-wedged edges,
Even though the mouth is still.

But the eyes are in themselves
Though battered and tired
As his clothes are limp and dark,
His boots, beaten and weary.

He walks down the old stone steps,
Steadily and resigned and expectant.

Soft bread,
Cheese,
Tea and whisky
Are on his mind,

Maybe some heat
To help feed on this:
This quiet living towards the
Surreptitious dignity of isolation.

J.E. Natanson

DEPRESSION – LUNDY, PORTLAND; LOW; 40; FALLING

...and love, that ancient mortar, crumbling now.
no little child to save me from myself,
to stick heroic fingers in the dyke.
so fragile seem the stones and bricks of life...

the gean tree blossom's not so white this year.
I shudder touching broken flesh of bluebells.
all round the thrusting, grasping, greedy green.

a distant emperor, I watch my friends –
their gladiators' eyes clashing fierce
in empty talk over full wine glasses.

I feel so very tired every morning now.
I think, surely I've read this book before?
so trivial and haphazard seem
the bulwarks I've built up across the years.

out at sea storm clouds have gathered.
the ocean heaves its deep dissatisfactions.
I wait in dread this swollen springtime tide.
soon that first wave must break. swamp me.

in terror, I swim up and down the pool,
concentrating on each stroke, counting lengths
and reciting a charm against drowning.

Donny O'Rourke

GREAT WESTERN ROAD

Glasgow, you look beatific in blue
and I've a Saturday before me
for galleries and poems,
a house full of Haydn,
and beneath my kitchen window,
tennis stars in saris
lobbing backhands at the bins.
French coffee, and who knows maybe
Allen Ginsberg in my bath!
then round to the dairy
where scones are cooling on the rack
and Jimmy won't let me leave
till I've tried one there and then,
here, where the new Glasgow started –
an old grey city going blonde
whose Asian shops are full of fruits
we owe to Cap'n Bligh
and I'm so juiced I could walk clear
to Loch Lomond,
past buses stripping the willow
all along Great Western Road
but I just browse bargains in banjos
and pop art knitted ties,
before checking out the crime section
at Caledonian Books,
finding Freesias in the flowershops
and in the second hand record store,
Bruckner's Third,
The Cleveland
under Szell:
so sad; like falling for passing students
with that black haired, blue eyed look,
or buying basil and chorizos...

In the afternoon I'll look at paintings
in Dougie Thomson's Mayfest show,
maybe stroll down to the studio
to view some archive film,
past the motorways and multi-storeys
of Grieve's Ultimate Cowcaddens,
the peeling pawn at George's Cross
where, today, everything is redeemable
because tonight there'll be guitar poets
from Russia at the Third Eye Centre.
And later I'll cook zarzuela
for a new and nimble friend.
God Glasgow it's glorious
just to gulp you down in heartfuls,
feeling something quite like love.

Janet Paisley

DUE

It's early moarnin an the mist's risin aff the gress, hingin ablow the trees like a curtin fae thur branches. It suits me. Ah'm no in masell. A coo lous wi burth pain faur doon the holla. A wey aff fae cauvin, bit kennin it. Ma feet ur sodden yit thurs nae mindin in me. Mibbe the harr is passin through me tae.

Only the shoatgun is soalid. Heaviur, greyur, cauldur. Soalid, richt enough. It cairryin me. Cairryin me doon the field, ower the burn's ruckled stanes, through its white watter an up by the mill.

Thurs nae a sowl aboot an ah leuk back tae see a licht cum oan in yin hoose. Rab Coannell gittin up fur the post. Ah keep ahint the mill, doon tae the coattages. The weeds ur high here an thur wetness wid tie thum roon me. Ye jist keep shuvin.

Ootside his hoose thurs nae back gairden. Jist the wildness an the wet. Close tae the stanes huv the braith o the wurld oan thum. A licht goes oan it ma shouder, dull yella. Watter rins, tinny, intae a kettle. Thur is whustlin. Saft, nae tune, mind elsewhaur whustlin. Ah dinnae waant these meenuts o his day. The waashin. The tea made, drunk. Ah waant the slammin o his door. Feet oan his graivel path. The key in his gairidge padloak. Ah waant the leuk oan his face is he turns roon.

138

Ruaraidh MacThòmais

CHERNÒBYL

Thàinig e a-nuas às an adhar gun fhiosda,
gun fhaicinn, gun fhaireachdainn,
is shiab e steach dha na pòirean,
dha na ceallan, a' cruth-atharrachadh
an stèidh, a' dèanamh aimhreit
far a robh còrdadh,
ag at 's a' seacadh 's a' bòcadh,
a' cur leas gu aimhleas
's ag atharrais
air ceòl an dòchais,
's thuirt feadhainn
a bha ri farchluais air rudan faisg orr'
gur h-e bh' ann an t-ainteas
a bhrùchd à toll-dubh Chernòbyl.

Ach bha cuid ann,
as bith ciamar a thuig iad,
a chunnaic dubhar
air an adhar
mus deach an toll-dubh 'na smàl
's aig a robh dùil
ri dubhachas
mar a bhà.

Derick Thomson

CHERNOBYL

It fell from the sky, unnoticed,
unseen, unfelt,
and intruded into the pores,
and the cells, changing
their foundations, producing conflict
where there had been agreement,
swelling and shrivelling and bulging,
turning benefit to misfortune
and mocking
the music of hope,
and some
who kept a close ear to the ground
said it was the super-heat
that erupted from the black hole of Chernobyl.

But there were some
who saw darkness
in the sky,
however it was they knew,
before the black hole began to smoulder
and who expected
darkness
anyway.

Valerie Thornton

COLD FEET

After August's monsoons
this Indian summer
has confused the gilded doos
into flurries of fluttering
upon the Great Eastern's gutters.

This foolish spring is passing
and, like the unerring arrows
of departing geese, you are moving on.

There is winter in the long shadows.
Time to shake the feathers
up the duvet and seek the comfort
of socks in bed.

THE OTHER SIDE OF THE COIN

Never missed a trick
when I played my loose joints.

I laid my thumb along my wrist,
kinked my fingers
and had them in stitches
when I stood on my hands
and hung my legs over my shoulders
balancing
in a young circle of laughter.

I'm still pretty good,
slipping discs at the drop of a hat
or plate.

I can creep for miles, all night,
back and forth,
between the bookcase and the kitchen sink,
trailing a flock of pain-birds
ready to roost, claws clamped,
whenever I stop.

And no-one sees the brightness
of this orange pain
or how many pills I can take
to cool it to blue.

They don't know
what they're missing.

142

Billy Watt

Clear Salt Water

Bruised air billows like a sea breeze
through the automatic doors
of this building that butts the sky
like an upended girder.

In the white ward we find him marooned
by an error of the brain.
His thin breath hardly flaws the silence.
There is only the faint pulse
as bubbles of salt water drip
from a limpid sac on a hook.

His nerveless head is propped towards
the Clydeside hills. Below, the last street
we had lived in as a family
has become the hospital car park.

As sunlight clouds the unwashed windows
his eyes flicker.
                We bend to the thin
stream of his breath ... but cannot tell
if he wants the curtains drawn.

All that we can hear is the drip
of clear salt water
from a calibrated sac.

Newton's First Law of Emotion

Go on then: incapacitate
my capacitators. Rotate
my Foucault pendulum.
Interfere with my so so
solid state of man.
Paddle with your fingers
in the ripple tank
of my emotions.
                    Take this
bundle of vibrations
I call myself
and make it oscillate
with a trembling that is –
though it is questionable
whether this can be verified
in any scientific way –
undeniably human.

A CLEARANCE

The unique detritus you find afterwards:
empty Rizla packets, a broken watch
in each drawer, child's lollipop drawings;
odd slippers compressed like leaves between pages ...

First of all we sifted through the drift
of empty envelopes, cheques from closed accounts,
reread our own Christmas messages.

Secondly we unmoored the furniture,
stacked it like a bonfire in the bedroom.
Behind the fireplace lay last week's coupon
with its eight spider kisses from eleven.

Out on the firth we could see a submarine
cruising like a basking shark from Faslane.

The rest we gathered in green plastic bags.

The naked floorboards, scarved with blue dust,
were as pale as your face in the coffin.

Irvine Welsh

THE FIRST DAY OF THE EDINBURGH FESTIVAL

Third time lucky. It was like Sick Boy telt us: you've got tae know what it's like tae try tae come off before you can actually dae it. You can only learn through failure, and what you learn is the importance of preparation. He could be right. Anyway, this time I've prepared. A month's rent in advance on this big, bare room overlooking the Links. Cash on the nail! Parting wi' that poppy was the hardest bit. The easiest was my last shot, taken in my left arm this morning. I needed something to keep us gaun during this period of intense preparation. Then I was off like a rocket around the Kirkgate, whizzing through my shopping list.

Ten tins of Heinz tomato soup, 8 tins of mushroom soup (all to be consumed cold), 1 large tub of vanilla ice cream (which will melt and be drunk), 2 bottles of Milk of Magnesia, 1 bottle of paracetamol, 1 packet of Rinstead mouth pastilles, 1 bottle of multivits, 5 litres of mineral water, 12 Lucozade isotonic drinks and some magazines: softporn, 'Viz', 'Scottish Football Today', 'The Punter' etc. The most important item had already been procured from a visit to the parental home, my Ma's bottle of valium, removed from her bathroom cabinet. I don't feel bad about this. She never uses them now, and if she needs them her age and gender dictate that her radge GP will prescribe them like jelly tots. I lovingly tick off all the items on my list. It's going to be a hard week.

My room is bare and uncarpeted. There is a mattress in the middle of the floor with a sleeping bag on it, an electric bar fire, and a black and white telly on a small wooden chair. I have three brown, plastic buckets, half filled with a mixture of disinfectant and water, for my shite, puke and pish. I line up my tins of soup, juice and my medicines within easy reach of the makeshift bed.

I took my last shot in order to get me through the horrors of the shopping trip. My final score will be used to make me sleep, and ease me off the scag. I'll try to take it in small, measured doses. I need some quickly. The great decline is setting in. It starts as it generally does, with a slight nausea in

the pit of my stomach and an irrational panic attack. As soon
as I become aware of the sickness gripping me, it effortlessly
moves from the uncomfortable to the unbearable. A tooth-
ache starts to spread from my teeth into my jaws and my eye
sockets, and all through my bones in a miserable, implacable,
dehabilitating throb. The old sweats arrive on cue, and let's
not forget the shivers, covering my back like a thin layer of
autumn frost on a car roof. It's time for action. No way can I
crash out and face the music yet. I need the old 'slowburn', a
soft come-down input. The only thing I can move for is scag.
One small dig to unravel those twisted limbs and send me off
to sleep. Then I say goodbye to it. I go to phone Raymie from
the payphone in the hall.

I am aware that as I dial, someone has brushed past me. I
wince from the fleeting contact, but have no desire to look
and see who it is. I have not met any of my 'flatmates' yet.
The fuckers don't exist for me. Nobody does. Only Raymie.
The money goes down. A lassie's voice. 'Hello?' she sniffs.
Has she got a summer cauld or is it scag?

'Is Raymie thaire? It's Mark here.' Raymie has evidently
mentioned me because although ah dinae ken her, she sure as
fuck kens me. Her voice chills over. 'Raymie's away,' she says.
'London.'

'London? Fuck... when's he due back?'

'Dinae ken.'

'He didnae leave anything fir us, did eh?'

'Naw...'

I put the phone down shakily. Two choices. One: tough it
oot, back in the room. Two: phone that cunt Forrester and go
to Muirhouse, get fucked aboot and ripped off with some crap
gear. No contest. In twenty minutes it was 'Muirhoose pal?' to
the driver on the 32 bus and quiveringly sticking my 45p into
the box. Any port in a storm, and it's raging in here behind my
face. An auld boot gies me the evil eye as I pass her on my way
down the bus. No doubt I am fuckin boggin and look a real
mess. It doesnae bother me. Nothing exists in my life except
myself and Michael Forrester and the sickening distance
between us, a distance being steadily reduced by this 32 bus.

I sit on the back seat, downstairs. The bus is almost empty.
A girl sits across from me, listening to her Sony Walkman. Is
she good looking? Who fuckin cares. Even though it's sup-

posed to be a 'personal' stereo, I can hear it quite clearly. It's playing Bowie... 'Golden Years'.

> *Don't let me hear you say life's takin' you nowhere –*
> *Angel...*
> *Look at those skies, life's begun, nights are warm and*
> *the days are yu–hu–hung...*

I've got every album Bowie ever made. The fuckin lot. Tons o' fuckin bootlegs n' awe. I don't give a fuck about him or his music. I only care about Mike Forrester, an ugly talentless cunt who has made no albums. Zero singles. But Mikey baby is the man of the moment. As Sick Boy once said, doubtlessly paraphrasing some other fucker: nothing exists outside the moment. (I think some radge on a chocolate advert said it first.) But I can't even endorse these sentiments as they are at best peripheral to the moment. The moment is me, sick, and Mikey, healer.

Some auld cunt – they're always on buses at this time – is fartin and shitein at the driver, firing a volley of irrelevant questions about bus numbers, routes and times. Get the fuck oan or fuck off and die ya foostie auld cunt. I almost choked in silent rage at her selfish pettiness and the bus driver's pathetic indulgence of the cunt. People talk about youngsters and vandalism, what about the psychic vandalism caused by these old bastards? When she finally gets oan the auld fucker still has the cheek tae huv a gob on her like a cat's erse. She sits directly in front of me. My eyes burrow intae the back of her heid. I'm willing her to have a brain haemorrhage or a massive cardiac arrest... no. I stop and think. If that happened, it would only delay me further. Hers must be a slow suffering death, to pay her back for my fuckin suffering. If she dies quickly, it will give people the chance to fuss. They will always take that opportunity. Cancer cells will do nicely. I will a core of bad cells to develop and multiply in her body. I can feel it happening... but it's my body it's happening to. I'm too tired to continue. I've lost all hate for the old doll. I only feel total apathy. She's now outside the moment.

My head is going down. It jerks up so suddenly and violently, I feel it's going to fly off my shoulders onto the lap of the testy auld mare in front of me. I hold it firmly in both hands,

elbows on knees. Now I'm going to miss my stop. No. A surge
of energy and I get off at Pennywell Road, opposite the shopping centre. I cross over the dual carriageway and walk
through the centre. I pass the steel-shuttered units which have
never been let and cross over the car park where cars have
never parked. Never since it was built. Over twenty years ago.
Forrester's maisonette flat is in a block bigger than most in
Muirhouse. They are typically two stories high, but his is five,
and therefore it has a lift, which does not work. To conserve
energy I slide along the wall on my journey up the stairs.

In addition to cramps, aches, sweats and an almost complete disintegration of my central nervous system, my guts
have also gone. I feel a queasy shifting taking place, an omin-
ous thaw in my long period of constipation. I try to pull
myself together at Forrester's door. But he will know I'm suffering. An ex-scag merchant always knows when someone is
sick. I just don't want the bastard knowing how desperate I
feel. While I would put up with any crap, any abuse, from
Forrester to get what I need, I don't see the sense in advertising
it to him more than I can help.

I have distinctive ginger hair and Forrester can obviously
see my reflection through the wire and dimpled-glass door. He
takes an age to answer. The cunt has started fuckin me aboot
before I even set fit in his hoose. He does not greet me with
any warmth in his voice. 'Awright Rents?' he says.

'No' bad Mike.' He calls me 'Rents' instead of Mark, I call
him Mike instead of 'Forry'. He's calling the shots. Is trying to
ingratiate myself to this cunt the best policy? It's probably the
only one at the moment.

'Moan in,' he tersely shrugs and I dutifully follow him.

I sit on the couch, beside but a bit away from a gross
bitch with a broken leg. Her plastered limb is propped up on
the coffee table and there is a repulsive swell of white flesh
between the dirty plaster and her peach coloured shorts. Her
tits sit on top of an oversized Guinness pot, and her brown
vesty top struggles to constrain her white flab. Her greasy,
peroxide locks have an inch of insipid grey-brown at their
roots. She makes no attempt to acknowledge my presence but
lets out a horrendous and embarrassing donkey-like laugh at
some inane remark Forrester makes, which I don't catch,
probably concerning my appearance. Forrester sits opposite

me in a worn-out armchair, beefy faced but thin bodied, almost bald at 25. His hair loss over the last two years has been phenomenal. Normally I would make a bitchy comment, but at the moment I would rather slag my favourite auntie about her colostomy bag. Mikey is, after all, my man. In the other chair next to Mikey is an evil looking bastard, whose eyes are on the bloated sow, or rather the unprofessionally rolled joint she is smoking. She takes an extravagantly theatrical toke, before passing it on to the evil-looking bastard. I've got fuck all against dudes with dead insect eyes set deep in keen, rodent faces. They are not all bad. It's this boy's clathes that give him away and mark him out as wideo extraordinaire. He has obviously been residing in one of the Windsor group hotels: Saughton, Bar L, Perth, Peterhead etc., and has apparently been there for some time. Dark blue flared troosers, black shoes, a mustard polo neck with blue bands at the collar and cuffs, and a green parka (in this fuckin weather!) draped over the back of the chair.

No intros are made, but that's the prerogative of my baw-faced icon, Mike Forrester. He's the man in the chair, and he certainly knows it. The bastard launches into this spiel, talking incessantly, like a bairn trying to stay up as late as possible. Mr Fashion, Johnny Saughton I'll call him, says nothing, but smiles enigmatically and occasionally rolls his eyes in mock ecstasy. If you ever saw a predator's face, it was Saughton's. The Fat Sow, god she is grotesque, hee-haws and I force out the odd sycophantic chuckle at times I gauge to be roughly appropriate.

After listening to this shite for a while, my pain and nausea force me to intervene. My non-verbal signals are contemptuously ignored, so I steam in. 'Sorry tae interrupt ye mate, but ah need tae be pittin ma skates oan. Ye goat the gear thaire?'

The reaction is over the top, even by the standards of the crappy game Forrester is playing.

'You shut yir fuckin mooth! Fuckin radge. Ah'll fuckin tell you whin tae speak. Just shut yir fuckin erse. You dinny like the company, you kin git tae fuck! End o' fuckin story.'

'Nae offence mate...' It's all tame capitulation on my part. After all, this man is a god to me. I'd walk on my hands and knees through broken glass for a thousand miles tae use the cunt's shite as toothpaste and we both know it. I am but a

pawn in a game called 'The Marketing Of Michael Forrester
As A Hard Man'. To all those who know him, it's a game
based on ridiculously flawed concepts. It's obviously being
played for Johnny Saughton's benefit, but what the fuck, it's
Mike's gig, and I asked to be dealt a shite hand when I dialled
his number.

I take some more crass humiliation for what seems like an
eternity. I get through it nae bother though. I love nothing
(except junk), I hate nothing (except forces that prevent me
getting any) and I fear nothing (except not scoring). I also
know that a shitein cunt like Forrester would never put me
through all this bullshit if he intended holding out on me. It
gives me some satisfaction remembering why he hates me.
Mike was once infatuated by a woman who despised him. A
woman I subsequently shagged. It hadn't meant a great deal to
either myself or the woman concerned, but it certainly bugged
the fuck out of Mike. Now most people would put this down
to experience, you always want what you can't have and the
things you don't really give a toss about, you get handed to
you on a plate. That's life, so why should sex be different from
any other part of it? I have had, and brushed off, such reverses
in the past. Every cunt has. The problem is that this shite's
intent on hoarding trivial grievances, like the fat-chopped
malignant squirrel that he is. But I still love him. I have to.
He's the boy holdin.

Mikey grows bored with his humiliation game. For a sad-
ist, it has all the interest of sticking pins into a plastic doll. I'd
love to have given him some better sport but I'm too fucked
to react to his dull-witted jibes. So he finally says: 'Goat the
poppy?'

I pull out some crumpled notes from my pockets, and
with touching servility, flatten them out on the coffee table.
With an air of reverence and all due deference to Mikey's
status as the man, I hand them over. I note for the first time
that the Fat Sow has, drawn on her plaster in thick black
marker pen, a huge arrow on the inside of her thigh pointing
towards her crotch. The letters alongside it spell out in bold
capitals: INSERT COCK HERE. My guts do another quick
birl, and the urge to take the gear from Mikey with maximum
force and get to fuck out of there is almost overwhelming.
Mikey snaffles the notes and to my surprise, produces two

white capsules from his pocket. I'd never seen the likes of them before. They were hard, wee, bomb-shaped things with a waxy coat on them. A powerful rage rolled over me, seemingly coming from nowhere. No, not from nowhere. Strong emotions of this type can only be generated by junk or the possibility of its absence. 'What the fuck's this shite?'

'Opium. Opium suppositories.' Mickey's tone has changed. It's cagey, almost apologetic. My outburst has shattered our sick symbiosis.

'What the fuck do ah dae wi these?' I says, without thinking, and then break out in a smile as it dawns on me. It lets Mikey off the hook.

'Dae ye really want me tae tell ye?' he sneers, reclaiming some of the power he'd previously relinquished, as Saughton sniggers and Fat Sow brays. He sees that I am not amused however, so he continues. 'Yir no bothered aboot a hit, right? Ye want something slow, tae take away the pain, tae help ye git oaf the junk right? Well these are perfect. Custom-fuckin-designed for your needs. They melt through yir system, the charge builds up, then it slowly fades. That's the cunts they use in hoespitals, fir fuck sakes.'

'Ye reckon these then man?'

'Listen tae the voice o' experience.' He smiles, but more across at Saughton than at me. Fat Sow throws her greasy head back and screeches, exposing large, yellowing teeth.

So I do just as recommended. I listen tae the voice o' experience. I excuse myself, retire to the toilet and insert them, with great diligence, up my arsehole. It was the first time I've ever stuck my finger up my own arsehole, and a vaguely nauseous feeling hits me. I look at myself in the bathroom mirror. Red hair, matted but sweaty, a white face with lots of disgusting spots. Two particular beauties, which really have to be classified as boils. One on the cheek, and one on the chin. Fat Sow and I would make an excellent couple, and I have a perverse vision of us in a gondola on the canals of Venice. I return downstairs, still sick, but high from scoring.

'It'll take time.' Forrester gruffly observes, as I swan back into the living room.

'You're tellin' me. For awe the good they've done ah might as well have stuck them up ma erse.' I get my first smile from Johnny Saughton for my troubles. I can almost see the blood around his twisted mouth. Fat Sow looks at me as if I had just ritually slaughtered her first born. That pained, incomprehensible expression of hers makes me want to pish my keks with laughter. Mike wears a very hurt I-crack-the-jokes-here look, but it is tinged with resignation through the realisation that his power over me has gone. It ended with the completion of the transaction. He was now no more to me than a lump of dugshite in the shopping centre. In fact, considerably less. End of story.

'Anyway, see yis later folks.' I nod over to Saughton and Fat Sow. A smiling Saughton gives me a matey wink which seems to sweep in the whole room. Fat Sow even tries to force a smile. I take their gestures as further evidence that the balance of power between Mike and myself has fundamentally shifted. As if to confirm this, he follows me out the room, dropping his voice as I step out of the flat. 'Eh, ah'll see ye aroond man. Eh... sorry aboot awe that shite ah wis hittin ye wi in thaire. That cunt Donnelly... he makes me dead jumpy. A fuckin heidbanger o' the first order. Ah'll tell ye the fill story later. Nae hard feelins though, eh Mark?'

'Ah'll see ye.' I reply, my voice hopefully carrying enough promise of threat to cause him a little bit of unease, if not concern.

By the time I hit the bottom of the stair I've forgotten all about my sickness, well almost. I can feel it, the ache through my body, it's just that it doesn't really bother me any more. I know it's ridiculous to con myself that the gear is making an impact already, but there's definitely some placebo effect taking place. One thing that I am aware of is great fluidity in my guts. It feels like I am melting inside. I have not shat for about five or six days. Now it seems to be coming. I fart, and instantly follow through, feeling the wet sludge in my pants with a quickening of my pulse. I slam on the brakes, tightening my sphincter muscle as much as I can. The damage has been done, however, and will get much worse if I don't take immediate action. I consider going back to Forrester's, but I want nothing more to do with the twat for the time being. I remember that the bookies in the shopping centre has a toilet at the back.

I enter the smoke-filled shop and head straight to the bog. What a fuckin scene. Two guys stand in the doorway of the toilet, just pishing into the place which has a good inch of stagnant, spunky urine covering the floor. It is oddly reminiscent of the foot pool at the swimming baths I used to go to. The two punters shake their cocks in the passage and stuff them into their flies with as much care as you'd take putting a dirty hanky into your pocket. One of them looks at me suspiciously and bars my path to the toilet. 'Bog's fuckin blocked mate. Ye'll no' be able tae shite in that.' He gestures to the seatless bowl full of brown water, toilet paper and lumps of floating shite. I look sternly at him, 'Ah've goat tae fuckin go mate.'

'Yir no' fuckin shootin up in thaire ur ye?' Just what I needed. Muirhouse's Charles Bronson. Only this cunt makes Charles Bronson look like Michael J. Fox. He actually looks a bit like Elvis – like Elvis does now – a chunky, decomposing ex-Ted.

'Away tae fuck.' My indignation must have been convincing, because this radge actually apologises.

'Nae offence meant pal. Jist some o' they young cunts in the scheme huv been tryin tae make this thir fuckin shootin gallery. We're no intae that.'

'Fuckin wideo cunts,' his mate added.

'Ah've been oan the fuckin peeve fir a couple o' days mate. Ah'm gaun fuckin radge wi the runs here. Ah need tae shite. It looks fuckin awfay in thaire, but it's that or ma fuckin keks. Ah've nae shit oan me. Ahm fuckin bad enough wi the bevvy, nivir mind anythin' else.' My way is swiftly unblocked. I feel the pish soak into my trainers as I step over the door ridge. I reflect on the ridiculousness of saying I had no shit on me when my keks are full of it. One piece of good luck though, is that the lock on the door is intact. Truly remarkable, considering the atrocious state of the bogs.

I whip off my keks and sit on the cold, wet porcelain chunky. I empty my guts, feeling as if everything, bowel, stomach, intestines, spleen, liver, kidneys, heart, lungs and fucking brains are all falling through my arsehole into the bowl. As I shit, flies batter off my face, sending shivers through my body. I grab at one, and to my surprise and elation, feel it buzzing in my hand. I squeeze tightly enough to immobilise it. I open my mitt and see a huge, filthy bluebottle, a big, furry currant of a bastard. I smear it against the wall opposite, tracing out an 'H' then an 'I' then a 'B' with my index finger, using its guts, tissue and blood as ink. I start on the 'S' but my supply grows thin. No problem. I borrow from the 'H' which has a thick surplus, and finish the 'S'. I sit as far back as I can without sliding into the shit-pit below me, and admire my handiwork. The vile bluebottle, which caused me a great deal of distress, has been transformed into a work of art which gives me much pleasure to look at. I am speculatively thinking about this as a positive metaphor for other things in my life, when the realisation of what I have done sends a paralysing jolt of raw fear through my body. I sit frozen for a moment. But only a moment.

I fall off the pan, my knees splashing onto the pishy floor. My jeans crumple to the deck and greedily absorb the urine, but I hardly notice. I roll up my shirt sleeve and only hesitate briefly, glancing at my scabby and occasionally weeping track marks, before sticking my hands into the brown water. I rummage fastidiously and get one of my bombs back straight away. I rub off some shite that's attached to it. A bit melted, but largely intact. I stick it on top of the cistern. Locating the other takes several long dredges through the mess and the pan-handling of the shite of many good Muirhouse and Pilton punters. I gag once, but get my white nugget of gold, surprisingly even better preserved that the first. The feel of water on my skin disgusts me even more than the shite. My brown stained arm reminds me of getting tanned but keeping a t-shirt on. It's right up past my elbow as I had to go right around the bend. Despite my discomfort at the feel of water on my skin, it seems appropriate to run my arm under the cold tap at the sink. It's hardly the most extensive or thorough wash I've had, shite still stuck under my fingernails, but it's all I can stand. I then wipe my arse with the clean part of my pants and chuck the shite-saturated keks into the bowl beside the rest of the waste.

I hear a knocking at the door as I pull on my soaking Levis. It's the sense of wetness on my legs, again, rather than the stench, which makes me feel a bit giddy. The knocking becomes a loud bang. 'C'moan ya cunt. Wir fuckin burstin oot here.'

'Hud yir fuckin hoarses.'

I was tempted to swallow the suppositories, but I rejected this notion almost as soon as it crossed my mind. They were designed for anal intake, and there was still enough of that waxy stuff on them to ensure that I'd have, in all probability, a difficult job keeping them down. As I'd shot everything out of my bowel, my boys were probably safer back there. Home they went.

I got some funny looks as I left the bookies, not so much from the pish-queue gang who piled past me with a few derisory 'aboot-fuckin-time-in-awes' but from one or two punters who clocked my wasted appearance. One radge even made some vaguely threatening remarks, but most were engrossed in the form cards, or the racing on the screen. I noted Elvis/Bronson was gesticulating wildly at the telly as I left.

At the bus stop, I realised what a sweltering hot day it had become. I remembered somebody said that it was the first day of the Festival. Well, they certainly got the weather for it. I sat on the wall by the bus stop, letting the sun soak into my wet jeans. I saw a 32 coming, but didn't move, through apathy. The next one that came, I got it together to board the fucker and headed back tae Sunny Leith. It really is time to clean up, I thought, as I mounted the stairs of my new flat.

Brian Whittingham

THEORY

What YOU need
        is a Stephen Hendry 16 ounce screw in cue
        with a leather tip – 5/16 inch diameter,
        crouch over the table
        with left leg flexed and right leg straight,
        you must only move
        the lower right arm from a pivot point
        at the right elbow
        in a pendulum like motion

What YOU need
        is Severiano Ballesteros graphite shafted clubs,
        and golf balls,
        weight not greater than 1.62 ounces
        diameter not less than 1.68 inches,
        the maxifly longflight type
        with concave dimples
        that guarantee
        no slicing or hooking,
        ALWAYS keep your head down
        with your left arm straight at all times
        and your club face perpendicular to the ball

What YOU need
        is Reebok attack football boots
        backed up by Nike pump action trainers
        with an Adidas TANGO ball,
        five yards faster and swerves a lot easier
        and an Umbro designer kit
        that makes you feel like an Italian
        even though you look like a Glaswegian,
        make the ball do the work
        and take note
        'No one remembers the losers'

What YOU need
is adjustable speedo goggles,
remove all body hair to lessen friction
spread fingers apart to aid propulsion
and exhale every second stroke
to optimise efficiency,
and if you get fed up with that
then completely empty your lungs of air
prior to jumping in the deep end
and you will find that
you can sit on the bottom for as long as you
want without ever floating to the top.

SCREAM IF YOU WANT TO GO FASTER

When the noise gets louder
and the crowds grow thick,
when the rides spin faster
and end so quick

      the shifty
      SUPERBOB attendant
      gives your change in
      precise neatly folded notes
      that add up to nine for him,
      and seven for you

as the anticipation
of your day
gets drowned
by
empty metal buckets, with bouncing wooden balls
by
red plastic rings, that never circle glittering prizes
by
rifles with telescopic sights, that ensure you never
knock the clay pigeon from its perch
by
bingo playing fanatics, waiting on one
by
bubble light darts, that never find their target
by
gigantic football team balloons, that parents always carry
by
the jumbo juicy hot dogs, smothered in fried ketchup onions
by
voices in the air
telling you to

SCREAM

if you want to go faster.

David G.R. Young

THE ROAD BACK

Maybe Samuel Johnson had been right. It could just be that the best opportunity afforded to a young Scotsman was the road out of Scotland. At one time I would have had to agree, when things were going well for me, and life winked at me as I winked back. Now I'm not sure one way or t'other.

When I left Scotland it was a country hanging, drawing and quartering itself in its own industrial effluvia. It excavated the rock on which the very land stood, and shipped it out.But I knew then, as I know all the more so now, that a country which decides to sell itself is not long for this world. That's why I left in the first place.

New Orleans in 1922 was a fine place for a young man to be. I worked the ships on that part of the Mississippi which lapped up to the Irish Channel. Although a Cajun appointed me, it was John Knox who made me a foreman, and I supervised the Kellys and the Murphys. If the truth be told, not that I would admit it in public, even now, I rather envied the Paddys their religion. For me a sin committed, whether whisky, women, or a similar impropriety, was done. But for the Paddys, oh for them, a sin was to be wallowed in, loved, and tortured, and then to be cleansed. All of which makes you wonder, in no little measure, about your relations to God.

If I think about it I could have done precisely the same thing at home, supervising the Keelies and Papes. The only difference being though, and a big difference it was too, was that in America I unloaded the ships. In the Irish Channel the ships disgorged their contents onto a hungry land. Back in Scotland, as I could never bring myself to dream about it, a country disgorged itself into a thousand silent holds. Aye, and not only its land, its animals, and its produce, but its people. And as Scotsman unloaded Scotsman they swarmed across the great territory of Canada, and the United States of America. Some ventured even deeper into the Americas, before my time of course, but what makes me so sure is that I aye detect a glimpse of calvinistic stoicism in the face of many a dictator of the southern lands.

But back to my story, afore I fall into the usual trap of the
old by distilling my experience into its essence instead of
telling it as well as I know, and letting God be my judge. My
first summer in New Orleans I learnt what real heat was. The
kind that cooks you from the inside, and does not subside
even as the moon appears. It was a heat that did not allow a
man his weakness. To take a guid drink was to invite all sorts
of demons into your head, and sins of the flesh, well, they
were not to be contemplated. Even the mongrels of the alley
were too stricken down to sniff around.

For a romantic it could be said that it was the summer
heat of the city that led me to meet Charlette. As the heat drew
up every drop of moisture from the ground, so something had
to give. And give it did as the storm clouds assembled themselves over the Big Easy.

I had escaped finally from the docks, as is the foreman's
lot, and had taken to a bar on Basin Street. As the clouds burst
so Charlette took refuge in the bar where I was now sitting.
Ebony rich in colour, she stood, just in the doorway of the bar.
It was her bad luck to be a pretty young black woman caught
in the wrong part of the French Quarter.

One of the men noticed her, and pulled her roughly into
the bar where the other men, Polaks, Czechs, and Micks
decided to purge the heat from their bodies, just as the sky
was now doing. As two of them held her down, and another
prepared to deliver himself to the Devil, my temper broke. I
had had no dealings with the Negroes, and no special love for
them as a people, but I could not allow this. I fought my way
through and the men off of her. It was something I could not
allow to happen.

Afterwards, in the room of a cheap hotel, she tended to a
cut on my forehead, as I lectured her on the inadvisability of a
woman of her colour venturing into such a place. A half hour
later as she was about to leave I felt the terrible urge come
over me, but instead I opened my mouth and screamed, letting
all the air out of my lungs. Yet still I wanted her, and so that is
how we found ourselves in a backstreet church of the Parish of
New Orleans, becoming man and wife.

After the ceremony we went back to the hotel room and I
pondered how I had come to marry a woman who knew no
more about me than I did about her. And a woman whose skin

was as coal black as mine was milky white. On that first night
we both lay motionless in the same bed. In the morning I
woke, and in a burst I consummated our marriage.

On the Monday we moved, together, back into my lodg-
ings, at least until I could find somewhere more suitable. From
then on at my work even my superior birth failed me, as I
endured the cracks of every Paddy I came into contact with. I
must have fired every man on my squad that week, and hired
them again just the same. By the end of the week I realised I
could stay there no longer.

I reckoned in my mind that the northern and eastern parts
of the country had to be better. So on the 1st of May in the
year of 1926 we arrived in New York, after a long train ride in
which my bride could not sit at one end of the train with me,
but where I could sit at the other with her.

New York afforded us little anonymity as it was after all a
city divided into neighbourhoods. We tried to live, as it was
the first place we found, in the Italian neighbourhood on
Elizabeth Street. It was a street where I found a group of more
tightfisted and tightminded bastards than my own: the
Sicilians. We lasted a week, as I ventured further and further
out of the neighbourhood for work with little success. The dis-
aster on Wall Street had not yet come but things were
noticeably tougher. People were giving to their own and this
time I found myself on the wrong end.

We soon upped and moved to Harlem where the Negro
lads viewed me with what seemed at the time, a primeval
hatred. Later I realised that had not fate taken me this way my
hatred on seeing a black man walk out with a white woman
would have been even greater. However they left us alone, and
for a time we were happier than we had been. Charlette glad
to be among her own, and me not caring one way or t'other.

But it could not last, as well I knew. One night as I
returned from the job that I had recently found at the docks I
wandered into a bar only two blocks from home. A surly
black bartender served me, but I felt trouble coming. A young
Southerner, no doubt recently escaped from the land with all
the suppressed anger that entailed, picked a fight with me. I
bludgeoned him to the ground with my fists but not before he
had cut my face with a jagged glass. As I left to walk home
the throbbing pain in my face reminded me just how much I

hated them. Those that would not give me peace.

It was on that short walk back that I took the great deci-
sion to return home to the place of my birth. Surely there I
thought I might be given some fair treatment. I knew I would
not receive a full acceptance but I still harboured some
romantic notion of the people to whom I belonged.

So Charlette, by now carrying our first, and myself took
our leave of America. Our first child was born on the voyage
across, thrown out a month early by the swell of the sea. All
the passengers on board, at least a good many, fussed over the
little mite, and by a miracle it was with us when we first
stepped back on to Scottish soil.

In no time at all we found ourselves in the Stirlingshire
village of the Redding, which in those times had a pit where I
thought myself bound to contract some work. What with the
coal dust blackening all that it touched in the village, which
was about near everything, I reckoned that one more black
face would not be such a change. And indeed at first we were
treated as a queer sight, but harmless none the less.

It took until September afore trouble really came calling.
All the faster to join the body of the Kirk I climbed up to the
manse one Saturday afternoon, to inquire as to the long over-
due christening of the child. I could hardly believe my ane ears
when the dour faced minister told me that such a ceremony
would not take place in his Kirk. I told him quickly enough
that the Kirk has aye seen all those who come to God as equal,
and I reminded him of the previous minister. He had gone, so
the villagers said, to convert the heathens in Africa. By that
reasoning, I asked him, what right did he have to deny my
child its birthright?

Despite all my protestations he was having none of it, and
as he went to push me out of the manse I struck him a blow
to his stupid, pious face. I knew it was wrong to do so but
had he not given me more than a little justification?

That blow however was to be my downfall. I was lifted in
the morning, as my crying wife and child looked on, and taken
to the court in Falkirk. The sheriff after listening to all the evidence declared me not only guilty but insane as well. I shouted
to him that he was a daft old bastard and was dragged out,
not truly believing what it all meant.

That is how I came to be in this place, no doubt my final

resting place. In the first few weeks here I waited for some word from Charlette. My waiting was in vain and as the time became months I began to lose hope. Now I sit among all the shouters and screamers, joining them occasionally to shout as I did an ocean ago in a New Orleans hotel room.

I do not know what has happened to my son, even whether he survived. All I know is that a man should be able to love who he chooses, and hate who he chooses as well no doubt. That is my story and that is its essence.

NOTES ON CONTRIBUTORS

Kate Armstrong, 46, has had poetry, prose and translations, English and Scots, published in various anthologies, periodicals and on radio and teaches in Dundee. **Elizabeth Burns's** book *Ophelia and other poems* was published this year by Polygon. **Ron Butlin** was born in 1949 in Edinburgh where he now lives. **Marianne Carey** was born in Glasgow in 1962 and has been writing ever since; plays, mostly. **Susan Chaney** lives in Edinburgh with her three children and is currently working hard to complete her first novel. **Barbara Clarke** is thirty something, living and working in Edinburgh, with aspirations to live and work in the USA and Central America. **Ken Cockburn** is a writer and theatre/visual arts administrator living in Edinburgh. **Thomas Queen Cunningham** was born in Kirkintilloch in 1949, left school at 16 with three 'O' levels and now lives in Glasgow where he works as a fireman and is at present studying English at North Kelvinside Secondary School as an adult pupil. **John Dixon,** who was born in Springburn, Glasgow, and has had work accepted by *Oxford Magazine, London Magazine, Poetry Review* and *Verse* and his first full collection published by *Polygon* in 1991, graduated from Edinburgh University and practised Law until leaving that profession to take up a LA Education post in Essex and to devote more time to writing. **Muriel Ferrier,** married with two grown daughters, trained at Dunfermline College of Physical Education and enjoys reading and writing in Scots and English. **Pete Fortune** lives in Dumfries and has been previously published in *Lallans, Chapman* and *West Coast Magazine.* **Raymond Friel,** born 1963, has had work published in *NWS5, NWS7, Verse* and *Gairfish,* and currently teaches in London. **Graham Fulton** is currently working on a follow-up collection to *Humouring the Iron Bar Man,* published by *Polygon* in 1990. **Robin Fulton's** latest collection of poems is *Coming Down to Earth and Spring is Soon* (Shearsman, Portsmouth and Oasis Books) and his latest translation is a second selection from the Norwegian of Olav Hauge (White Pine, Fredonia, NY). **Jane Harris** was born in Belfast in 1961 and recently returned to Glasgow after living and working in London, the French Alps and Lisbon. **A.L. Kennedy** lives in Glasgow and is author of the collection *Night Geometry And The Garscadden Trains.* **Norman Kreitman,** who until recently was engaged in medical research in Edinburgh, has published two books of poetry, *Touching Rock* (1987) and *Against Leviathan* (1989) both with Aberdeen University Press. **Tath Lardans** was born in 1969 and has an unemployed friend called Kirsty. **Brenda Leckie** lives in Glasgow and has had poems published in magazines *Akros, Chapman, Poetry Review* and in anthologies *Behind the Lines, New Poetry* and *New Writing Scotland.* **Douglas Lipton,** born in Glasgow in 1953 and educated at Strathclyde University, has lived in Dumfriesshire for fourteen years where he now works as a Learning Support/Special Needs teacher. **Linda McCann**, who lectures part-time, has published short stories as well as poetry, and has taught Creative Writing for Glasgow University and the Adult Education Department. **Mary McCann** comes from Ayrshire and lives in Edinburgh and likes her writing to have a social life, so goes to writing groups (e.g. Pomegranate), and reads in public when she gets the chance. **James McGonical** is Head of English in Jordanhill College of Education and is currently co-editing *Sons of Ezra: British Poets and Pound* with Michael Alexander. **Duncan McLean** is quite happy not to have any biography. **John Maley** was born in Glasgow in 1962 and is a poet and a playwright. **Angus Martin**, born in 1952 in Campbeltown, has had three books of social history published, and one of poetry, *The Larch Plantation*. **Linda Marquart** was born in Canada and was an opera singer before coming to Edinburgh, where she is engaged in writing her second novel. **Gordon Meade's** work due out this year includes *Walking Towards the Sea* (Villa Vic Press) and *Singing Seals* (Chapman New Writing Series). **Gus Morrison** is forty, happily married to Kathy and at present works in the John Wheatley College on part-time temporary contracts. **John Murray** is a 37 year old landscape architect in the Borders with poems in *The New Makars, New Writing Scotland, Chapman* and *Lallans*. **Thom Nairn** is managing editor of *Cencrastus* and is currently Writer in Residence for Ross and Cromerty district. **Jan Natanson** was born in Glasgow, lives in Kirriemuir, Angus, and writes plays and poetry in Scots and English. **Donny O'Rourke** is an arts producer with Scottish Television in Glasgow: *Second Cities*, his first book of poems, was published by the Vennel Press earlier this year. **Janet Paisley's** other publications include *NWS8, Original Prints III* and *IV, The New Makars, Gown, North Light, Scottish Child, Lines Review;* collected poems *Pegasus in Flight* (Rookbook), *Images* (Murray House); currently writing fellow, Glasgow District Libraries. **Derick Thomson** retires this year from the Chair of Celtic at Glasgow University and has been writing and publishing Gaelic poetry for the last fifty years. **Valerie Thornton** lives in Glasgow, teaches creative writing, subtitles for Ceefax, and has published poems and short stories in a wide variety of magazines and anthologies. **Billy Watt** was born in Greenock and now teaches and writes in West Lothian. **Irvine Welsh**, who lives in Leith, is currently completing a brightly optimistic novel full of sympathetic, generously spirited characters. **Brian Whittingham** writes and performs poetry and stand-up comedy with a collection of poetry, *Industrial Deafness*, about Clydeside shipyards recently published. **David G.R. Young**, 22, is a film-maker, freelance journalist and writer.